CHARLES VAN RIPER, editor   *Foundations of Speech Pathology Series*

Prentice-Hall Foundations of Speech Pathology Series

PRENTICE-HALL INTERNATIONAL, INC., *London*
PRENTICE-HALL OF AUSTRALIA, PTY., LTD., *Sydney*
PRENTICE-HALL OF CANADA, LTD., *Toronto*
PRENTICE-HALL OF INDIA (PRIVATE) LTD., *New Delhi*
PRENTICE-HALL OF JAPAN, INC., *Tokyo*
PRENTICE-HALL DE MEXICO, S.A., *Mexico City*

Speech Correction
in the Schools

MARTHA E. BLACK

Consultant, Speech Correction,
Division of Special Education,
State of Illinois

𝓍𝓍𝓍

Prentice-Hall, Inc., *Englewood Cliffs, N.J.*

Printed in the United States of America
82774-C

This book is dedicated
to the backbone of our profession,

the public school speech correctionist

editor's note

THE SET OF VOLUMES WHICH CONSTITUTES THE *Foundations of Speech Pathology Series* is designed to serve as the nucleus of a professional library, both for students of speech pathology and audiology and for the practicing clinician. Each individual text in the series is written by an author whose authority has long been recognized in his field. Each author has done his utmost to provide the basic information concerning the speech or hearing disorders covered in his book. Our new profession needs new tools, good ones, to be used not once but many times. The flood of new information already upon us requires organization if it is to be assimilated and if it is to help us solve the many different professional problems which beset us. This series provides that essential organization.

One of the unifying and outstanding features of all the volumes in this series is the use of search items. In addition to providing the core of information concerning his subject, each author has indicated clearly other sources having significance for the topic being discussed. The reader is urged to explore, to search, and to discover—and the trails are charted. In so rapidly changing a profession as ours, we cannot afford to remain content with what we have been taught. We must learn to continue learning.

Although each individual volume in this series is complete unto itself, the instructor should welcome the opportunity presented by the *Foundations of Speech Pathology Series* to combine several volumes to form the basic structure of the course he teaches. They may also be used as collateral readings. These short but comprehensive books give the instructor a thoroughly flexible teaching tool. But the primary aim of the authors of these texts has been the creation of a basic library for all of our students and professional workers. In this series we have sought to provide a common fund of knowledge to help unify and serve our new profession.

preface

THE AUTHOR HAS HAD THE PRIVILEGE OF ASSISTING IN THE BIRTH OF several hundreds of school speech programs. Through the years she has observed uncounted numbers of novices develop into professional workers. Because of these experiences an awareness of the need for better preparation of school therapists has become so obsessive that she has written this book. For it is in the schools where the greatest numbers of both the children and the resources are found, and it is also in the schools where most speech therapists will be employed. They must be trained for these positions. They must be better trained.

The early decades of school speech therapy were largely ones of experimentation. Through successes and failures we learned that certain procedures were more effective than others. Recognizing that the discovery and development of new ideas and concepts will always be a basic part of professional growth, we believe nevertheless that a thorough familiarity with the accumulated fund of knowledge and information concerning the school setting will aid the student in developing fresh approaches to the many problems found in school therapy.

At a time when all education is becoming concerned about the preparation of those who are to work in our schools, it is imperative that we in speech therapy give careful consideration to what is being offered to the students who are learning to become therapists. Vital as academic learning and clinical experiences are, they are *ix* not enough. They should be expanded and increased, it is true, but the student must also be prepared to function in the unique setting of the school. It is with the hope of contributing to that preparation that this book is written.

Many examples of activities and practices have been cited. We wish to caution the reader, however, that these are not offered as models of perfection but rather as descriptive reports rooted in reality. It is hoped that they will stimulate the student to devise better plans and better techniques.

I am deeply grateful to the many public school therapists, to the members of university clinics, and to the special education staff in the Illinois Office of the Superintendent of Public Instruction for the assistance and encouragement they have given in the preparation of this book. Every page reflects their thinking. A particular debt of gratitude is owed to my colleague, Milton Eastman, who through long months has given support that has been most essential; to Mary Swanston for her assistance in preparing illustrations; to my faithful secretary, Mrs. Elsie Means, whose competency has freed me of many responsibilities; and above all, to Dr. Charles Van Riper, whose pinpointed criticisms, jovial encouragements, and unfailing faith have brought the dream of a book on speech correction in the schools into a reality.

Martha E. Black

contents

Speech Correction in the Schools

SO YOU ARE GOING TO BE A SPEECH THERAPIST. YOU ARE ALLYING yourself with a profession whose origins are found in the very early history of mankind but whose maturity, as measured by recognition and breadth of service in our country at least, was delayed until the middle half of the twentieth century. It was in these years that a realization of the need for speech correction was dawning in a few universities and in a few public schools. People here and there were attempting to gauge this need and to experiment with plans for meeting it. In the late twenties a few state legislatures passed laws which made it possible to serve speech defective children in public schools. This movement grew gradually during the thirties and

1

the beginning

spurted forward in the forties. Today there is a nationwide acceptance of the educator's responsibility for the speech of all children but there are still vast areas in our country which have no services. In fact, the big majority of the school children are not yet reached. In a very real sense, you are, and through your entire professional life will be, a pioneer.

1   At the turn of the century what changes in educational philosophy and
    social conditions led to a concern for people with speech defects? Who
    were the first people to take action?
    Paul Moore and D. Kester, "Historical Notes on Speech Correction in the
    Pre-Association Era," *Journal of Speech and Hearing Disorders,* XVIII
    (February 1953), 48-53.

Our Name

The problem of what to call ourselves has long plagued our profession. How can a person best be designated who works to improve speech defects stemming from physical, psychological, or possibly environmental causes and who may work in a private office, in a hospital, in a clinic, but most likely in a school? Europeans have used the term "logoped" but in our country the name "speech correctionist" first found favor.

As time passed some objections to the term "correctionist" arose. There were persons who believed it was too negative a title. When research probed deeper into the causes of speech difficulties, it was evident that there was a preventative aspect to our service. Did the word "correctionist" encompass that idea? Could the task of developing speech that previously had not existed in the person be called correcting speech?

In an effort to find a name that would identify our work to the public, many suggestions have been made and a few used. For a time "clinician" was favored. While the people working in clinics and hospitals appeared to like it, many school people, particularly the administrators, believed this smacked too much of medical services and rejected it. The tendency to call all persons working in schools "teachers" has led to correctionists being known as the "speech teachers" and consequently being mistaken for teachers of general speech. The term "therapist" has gained more support, but it carries with it the chance of confusion and other professional difficulties. There are physical therapists and occupational therapists. These people carry out the physician's prescriptions. We do not. Some persons have desired "pathologist" as our title, but others have believed it covered only the medical aspect of the work. So on.

2   How are a "teacher" and a "therapist" differentiated?
     William C. Morse, "Teacher or Therapist," in Hountras, P. T., *Mental Hygiene* (Columbus, Ohio: Charles E. Merrill Books, Inc., 1961), pp. 523-26.

Although the author's personal preference is still the term "correctionist" because she believes that in the public schools it is the most descriptive and least objectionable title, it seems to be a bit

obsolete. In this book, therefore, "therapist" will be used most generally. According to Sheehan's research, it is the term overwhelm-
ingly preferred by most public school workers.

3   Which name for the profession in terms of the arguments of the following
    authors appears most valid to you? Tell why.
    Stanley Ainsworth, "Identity and Identification," ASHA, I (October 1959),
    45-46.
    Joseph Sheehan, "Professional Self-Image in Speech Pathology and Ther-
    apy," ASHA, III (December 1961), 423-25.
    James Curtis and others, "A Name for the Profession of Speech and Hear-
    ing," ASHA, IV (June 1962), 199-203.

Your Work Schedule

Someone whose identity has since been lost decided once that the
school children needing speech correction would be served best by
having two periods of therapy each week. Perhaps the same person
also decided that the length of the period should be between fifteen
and thirty minutes. Not too long after that a strong-willed group
promulgated the idea that the therapist needed half a day each week
in which to hold conferences, write lesson plans, catch up on records,
and prepare materials. No research studies contributed to the birth
of these policies, but amazingly they have had widespread acceptance, as is witnessed by the following findings.

National surveys show that 43 per cent of public school speech
therapists meet individual cases twice a week and 53 per cent meet
groups twice a week (13:39). A sizable number, however, meet individuals and also groups just once a week. Only 6 per cent meet
both individuals and groups more frequently. The same studies
show that 57 per cent of the group sessions last from 25 to 34
minutes, and 29 per cent utilize periods of from 15 to 24 minutes.
Sessions for individual therapy are shorter. Forty per cent devote
15 to 24 minutes for these and 36 per cent reported 25 to 34 minute
periods. Three out of four therapists thought the length of their
individual and group sessions approached the ideal. However, one
study showed that as much progress was made in once a week sessions as in two (42).

The policy requiring half a day for conference coordination or
office periods is followed by 52 per cent of the therapists (72:15;

Table 2-4). A few, 13 per cent, have a full day per week for this work, while the others either have no time or were not specific in their replies.

We thus learn that the common practice is for public school speech therapists to see their students twice a week for periods of 15 to 30 minutes and that the equivalent of half a day a week is reserved for office work. A few schools are experimenting with other plans. These will be reviewed following this section.

Your Case Load

What is the ideal case load? Perhaps it is the greatest number of children within the school situation who can be given maximum benefits of speech correction without appreciably shortening the life span of the therapist. But how is that number determined? There are several considerations involved and these differ from one locality to another.

The first is geography. A therapist who must travel time-consuming distances from district to district, or even from school to school, will be forced to serve fewer pupils than one who works within one or two schools. While every effort should be made to avoid traveling at times when school is in session, it is not possible always to do this.

The ages of pupils, grade placements, and types of defects must also be considered. If you find five first- and second-graders who have somewhat similar articulation problems, you might well schedule them as one group. Likewise you might find six or eight high-school stutterers who would respond well to group therapy. On the other hand, you might find that your six- or seven-year-old articulation cases came from classrooms which have already been separated on the basis of scholastic ability and so your particular pupils might not work well together. Again, you might find that because of other work in the school, you could not put your high-school people together. At this upper level the rigid scheduling of the regular classes will be your great obstacle.

If you work in a building that has classes for physically handicapped children you will have, in all likelihood, some cases who need intensive individual therapy. These, of course, will decrease the total number of pupils you can serve. Or, if you work in a system that cooperates with a college by furnishing opportunities for cadets to do student teaching, you may want to reduce the case load so that you may give time to their supervision.

The philosophy of the school administration concerning the speech program and which pupils it will serve will be no minor factor in the determination of your case load. It is not uncommon to hear an administrator of a first-year program pontifically announce, "We will apportion the correctionist's time according to the enrollment in each school and, if necessary, we will serve only the most severe cases." He, of course, has overlooked the fact that while enrollment is the most important single factor in estimating the number of speech cases to be found in a population, yet there may be other circumstances in a certain school that completely change the situation. An example of this would be a school that serves a newly developed area where many young families live. Three-quarters of the total enrollment might be in the first three grades; consequently, the speech load would be abnormally high. The superintendent has also failed to recognize the frequently proven truth that no one can select with unfailing accuracy the most severe cases. To date, no instrument has been developed that can do this efficiently and accurately. The superintendent, nevertheless, is the person who has the final responsibility for what is accomplished by your program and, incidentally, he is the one who pays the bills. We cannot ignore his opinion. Somehow you must help him understand, for he can be exceedingly helpful in making your work a success. He can also frustrate you if he misunderstands. Perhaps you can show him this book.

Should you encounter a situation in which the administrator and you do not see eye to eye regarding schedules and case loads, you of course must follow his directives, but you should begin a campaign to educate him to your point of view. Find opportunities to present your philosophy gently but firmly, and from time to time point up concrete examples of situations in which you believe your plan would have been an effective one. But, incidentally, never fail to show respect for his ideas. In this particular situation he might by chance be correct. If you are a tactful person and doing an honest job, eventually a workable plan will evolve. Compromises are the routes to change. Few perfect plans come to fruition.

A final consideration in the selection of a case load is a vital one but one that is all too frequently overlooked. It is the philosophy and skill of the correctionist. In every teaching situation there are two dominant factors. One is the pupil and the other is the teacher. The results of the encounter between the two are as dependent upon one as upon the other. Some of you will be able to carry larger case loads than will others. You may be better organizers or perhaps you may have greater vitality. Some of you will come from universities that have provided very complete preparation. Others may have failed you. Although shying away from tough jobs never made a great therapist, you should evaluate your abilities in a realistic fashion. There may be times when problems seem insurmountable, and you should seek the advice of your administrator. Never fear that admitting uncertainty marks you as a weak therapist. On the contrary, your recognition of what you do not know will increase your administrator's respect for your intelligence and integrity.

Experience * seems to indicate that therapists working in most school situations can serve at most about 70 to 100 pupils at any given time and still do a reasonably competent job. About 125 can be seen during a year. Unfortunately, the national average runs higher than these figures. One study reports the average case load to be about 130 children (72:20; Table 2-4). Another study reports that an average number of 111 children are seen weekly and 152 within the course of a year (13:36). In the same study about one-half of the therapists expressed concern over the size of their case loads, saying that the size does not approach the ideal they visualize.

Why do so many therapists say this? Let's do a little arithmetic. Four and a half days per week at five and a half hours a day mean 742 minutes twice a week. With 25 minutes for each group (20 minutes actual teaching), there are about 30 available periods. That means the groups in a total case load of 100 would have an average of three pupils a period. Since some children are to be seen individually, others will have to come in groups of five or six. The preparation and the record-keeping, too, are time-consuming jobs. Although some skilled therapists under favorable conditions have

* The writer is speaking of her own experience, which is considerable—she has visited approximately 1800 therapists over a period of seventeen years.

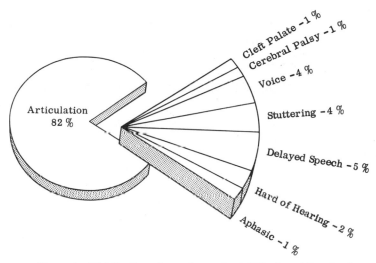

Figure 1. Distribution of speech case load, Illinois public schools, 1962-63.

served 100 pupils, the practice is not recommended. Case loads above 100 are a waste of both time and money and are unworthy of professional recognition.

The training of some therapists can contribute to feelings of frustration at large case loads. If the college offers opportunities for experience in therapy only in clinical settings, the therapist faces the school situation poorly prepared. A well supervised period of student teaching in a school with an established speech program will do much to acquaint the therapist with the opportunities and problems unique to the school situation.

In spite of these considerations, only when automation has made it possible to place a lisping child before a machine and later take him away with perfect speech will we be able to relax in our efforts to secure lower case loads.

Elementary school programs

Screening

Screening or surveying is the process of selecting cases with whom you will work. *Screening* usually means the examination of all children to select those whose speech is deviant enough to require therapy. The word *screening,* however, is used also to mean the process of selecting from this deviant group those who need immediate therapy. You will, therefore, do initial screening and secondary screening.

If you are the only therapist in a new district whose school enrollment is less than 1500 pupils, you may need to screen the entire group. In larger districts, however, complete screenings are unnecessary because far more speech defectives will be found than can be served by one therapist. Our profession is mature enough to venture an educated guess on the number of speech cases that will be found—about 7 to 8 per cent of a grade-school population and 2 to 4 per cent of a high-school group. When a choice of schools or grades must be made, the responsibility for doing so belongs to the administrator. You may wish to make a recommendation based on your specialized knowledge, but ask him to make the final decision. Although all children with speech problems have equal claims for your help, you can serve only a limited number. Arbitrary decisions must be made, and it is the administrator who must make them. He may, moreover, have information which indicates that a speech program will be better received in one spot than in another. You might not know this.

If you go into a district which has an established program, you will screen all beginners—kindergarteners or first-graders or both, all previously enrolled speech cases, and all other pupils enrolled for the first time in the school. Many systems also screen all fourth- or fifth-grade pupils; thus every child is seen by the therapist at least twice during the grade-school period. In addition to these groups you will want to test all pupils referred to you by teachers, principals, nurses, or other interested persons.

Teacher Referrals

Because it usually takes a teacher a month or two to become acquainted with her pupils, you may not want to ask for teacher referrals until about November. At the end of the first year, however, ask again for referrals. The teacher is now familiar with her pupils' speech and may make recommendations for your fall enrollment. In all school systems, even in those which have long established speech programs, it will be well to review with the teachers the reasons for referring a pupil to the therapist. There will always be new teachers who have never worked where speech services were available, and old teachers who are confronted with new problems. A few referral forms similar to the one in the following section may be given to the teachers after you have had an opportunity to talk with them individually or at a group meeting. Be certain to emphasize that over-referral is better than under-referral. Whether or not you take the referred child, thank the teacher for her interest and give her the reason for your decision.

Referral Forms

You may wish to devise a fairly detailed report for the teacher to complete. This type of referral has the advantage of focusing the teacher's attention on the exact characteristics of speech. In doing this she will become more interested in the problem. Many teachers, however, hesitate to commit themselves and often "His speech sounds funny to me" is as far as they will go. A card such as the following one will give the first essential information and is brief enough not to be considered a nuisance. In all cases, since you are the one who is going to have to make both the diagnosis and the case study, it may be more efficient to postpone the detailed questioning until the case is scheduled for therapy.

SPEECH REFERRAL CARD

School: _Lincoln_   Date: _9/23/63_

Name: _Alice Adams_   Grade: _5_

Teacher: _Margaret Halberg_   Room No.: _20_

Comments: _Difficult to understand. Voice weak and she chews her words._

Identification

This is a process of hearing the speech of all the pupils for the purpose of selecting those who, after a more careful diagnosis, may be given therapy. Since hundreds of children may be screened, the process should be as rapid as reasonable accuracy will permit. This means careful planning to eliminate waste motion.

Hopefully, you may have an opportunity to talk with the teachers, telling them either that you will hear the speech of every pupil or that you will test all former cases, all newly enrolled pupils, and possibly early referrals. In arranging your schedule, begin with the upper grades. Thus you will give the younger children time to become familiar with school procedures. After you have made a tentative plan, consult the building principal and the classroom teachers. Some changes may be necessary. When the schedule is established, send a note to each teacher stating what day and at what time you will be in her room.

From the speech files or from the school records, you will get the names and grade placements of all previously enrolled speech pupils. Make the list and check it at the office for accuracy. To this add the names and placements of pupils enrolled in the school for the first time. The first days of school are hectic ones for everyone. You may find both the teachers and the clerks too busy to give you much time; therefore, expect to wait a few days before getting all the names.

Now you are ready for your first face to face contact with the pupils. This is the most important thing you have had to do so far. Careful planning will do the trick.

Allow the teacher ten minutes to get the day started. Then, if speech therapy is an established program, step to the door of the first upper grade and ask to see one of the pupils whose name you have. You will find that upper-grade pupils will respond better in a speech situation if they are alone with you. So take the time needed to interview them individually in the speech room. When one goes back he can send the next one from his room, but you yourself had better call for the first one in each new room. Make a tentative decision in this first identification interview as to whether the pupils should be put on the list for the diagnostic secondary screening. A check sheet such as the following may be used:

INITIAL SCREENING

Date:_____9/6/63_____   School:_____Lincoln_____

                                      Grade:_____5_____

                                      Teacher:_____Miss Holtz_____

Name:	Speech Satisfactory	Type of Problem	Absent
Ann Andrews	x		
Sarah Gale		Stuttering	

This interview may be a very brief one. If your name is difficult to pronounce, teach it to the pupil, ask a few pleasant questions concerning himself, and have him read an easy paragraph which contains all the sounds. You may wish to devise one of your own or use one of the many found in all speech textbooks.

Give him the results of your decision regarding his speech and ask him to send the next pupil to you.

If yours is a new program in the school and you are testing every pupil, you will want to use a less time consuming procedure. Should the teacher fail to introduce you when you go into a room, do so yourself and tell the class very briefly why you are there and what will be the plan of procedure. Arrange to give the upper-grade pupils as much privacy as is consistent with the time available for the test. If there is a coatroom, an alcove, or a fairly quiet corridor, put up a small table, two chairs, and possibly a screen. You are in business. Make the list of the names from a previously obtained seating chart and have the pupils come to you in order. Ask each his name to avoid error. After a few questions, have him read a paragraph. If he shows hesitancy in reading, return to conversation. Then thank him for coming and tell him that will be all, or that you would like to see him again and will notify him of the time.

In the lower grades and where there is a previously established program, you may take the known speech cases in groups of three or four to the speech room for the tests. In a new program where you want to hear the speech of every pupil, you may have a table in the rear of the room and have the teacher arrange for some quiet work while you are interviewing the pupils. Unless the room is large enough for you to be fairly removed from the class, a screen will be useful. If it is impractical to test in either the room or the corridor, you may have to escort the children in groups to the speech room. To save time, begin by giving a demonstration of the testing procedure to the entire class. Everyone will then know what to expect. We observed one therapist in a large system do this very efficiently. After dramatizing for the entire class exactly what was to be done in the speech room, she took groups of six second-grade pupils and screened their speech in ten minutes. Curiosity may overcome timidity in the young child if you carry with you some mechanical toy such as a dog in a cage. Promise the children, "When you come to the speech room you will have a chance to let Spot out of his cage." Another way to put a frightened child at ease is to have him do something for you. "Will you please hold the door open while the other children come in?" or "Could you put the chairs all on one side of the table?"

Therapists do this initial screening in different ways and with different materials but we wish to remind you again that the basic purpose of this first contact with your children should be merely identification. You need to know which children need your services, the type of speech problem existing, and some indication of its urgency as far as therapy is concerned. In this initial screening, you do not have the time to make a complete diagnosis. That will come later. Your task is to evoke an adequate speech sample and to evaluate its deviancy.

After checking a child's name against your list, ask a few questions such as, "How did you come to school today?" "With whom?" "What pets do you have?" "What is your dog's name, color?" In a rapid screening, which is what the first one usually is, it is well to begin with the sounds most frequently defective. You might have for example pictures of a bar of soap, a ladder, a thumb, and a ring. One therapist had a little clown and animal figures to whom she gave names such as Lolly, Rigger, Soozel, Thump-Thump, Skitch, Figi, and Koto. She had them march around on a table and the children repeated their names.

You may find a few children who are shy about talking to grownups, but who will respond to a puppet. Have one handy. Almost any child will answer when Jocko says, "Hi, Johnnie, glad to see you here at school. I'm Jocko. Can you say Jocko?" "Let's count my buttons. One, two, three . . ."

Another easy way to stimulate speech is to show an interesting action picture (boy and dog chasing a ball) which will give a child an answer to the question, "What is happening here?" For older children, have sentences to read, such as "This girl thinks she can jump over the ditch." Most of your elementary texts in speech correction will suggest other test sentences.

The questions asked should be in the various interest ranges of the children. Examples: "Where does your Brownie or Cub Scout group meet?" "What TV program do you like best?" "Do you ride a bike to school? What are the traffic problems?" "Will we win the game Saturday? Why do you think so?"

Be alert to recognize a voice problem such as a pitch break, hoarse or husky voice, falsetto, hypernasality, and denasality. It is well for you to concentrate completely on voice for a sentence or two. Think of nothing else and have the pupil say, "There goes the man," "Shut the door," "The bell is ringing." In testing the voice of an older pupil, remember that it may change from hour to hour. You may have to depend upon referrals from other teachers for the more elusive cases. Here is where the vocal music teacher will be of assistance.

Stuttering is sometimes difficult to evoke in a survey. If the speech appears to be hesitant, controlled with a conscious effort, or has odd pauses, try pushing the pupil. "Hurry, I have many more to hear." Another trick is to ask him suddenly to say "banana, banana, banana." He might stutter if asked to tell what was happening in a story picture. In spite of everything you try, you may miss some stutterers, so impress upon the teachers their responsibility for referring these cases to you.

The cleft palate cases are usually quite apparent. Nevertheless, always observe carefully for excessive nasality and nasal emission.

These pupils should be given individual diagnosis in the therapy room. Do not embarrass them by too much questioning before others. The same is true of the cerebral palsy cases.

Then, too, there is yourself to consider. Regardless of the number of pupils you must screen, give yourself an occasional break in the routine. It is essential that each pupil sees in you a relaxed, wide-awake person who is interested in him. You can't be that if you are too weary.

When you have finished all the grades and picked up the absentees, you are ready for the kindergarten. By this time the teacher will be well enough acquainted with the children so that she has located those with extreme speech difficulties. You will want to see them and perhaps add them to your case load. Others, however, you may well ignore until the beginning of the second semester or even until the following fall. Maturity does a lot in these months.

4   A study of survey methods was made by this author:
     Vanetta R. Suydam, "Speech Survey Methods in Public Schools," *Journal of Speech and Hearing Disorders*, XIII (March 1948), 51-54.

Immature Speech

Much time and effort would be saved if we could identify immature speech which will disappear within months or possibly a year. Some people have argued that waiting to take a speech case until the fourth grade will increase efficiency and no one will suffer. What does it profit a child to have poor speech during the early years of his life? What is the reaction of most adults and some children to his speech? Will he be regarded as a sissy or possibly a child who is not too bright? Will she be kept a darling baby girl? Will either of them be given the responsibilities commensurate with their increasing ages? The unconscious reaction of most people to immature or defective speech is not one that is wholesome for the child. It may or may not do personality damage. The author was in a car with a superintendent of schools who was far more aware of children and their needs than most people. We stopped to ask directions from a handsome looking boy about eight years old. He stepped forward and gave the directions very accurately. As we drove away, I said, "He's a bright child." "Yes," the superintendent answered, "too bad he's a sissy." The boy lisped. If the instant and likely thoughtless reaction of that man was such, what will be the usual reaction of most other people?

It is our belief that it is far better to run the risk of giving speech correction to a few young children who might develop good speech without it (they'll not be with you long anyway) than to allow any child to suffer for even a few years, and possibly unconsciously, the reactions of society to poor speech.

To date, the articulation tests which have been devised for prognostic purposes have not proved to be practical instruments in a school situation.

> 5   What conditions offer some predictability of a child's speech growth patterns?
> Eunice T. Carter and McKenzie Buck, "Prognostic Testing for Functional Articulation Disorders Among Children in the First Grade," *Journal of Speech and Hearing Disorders*, XXIII (May 1958), 124-33.
> M. Steer and H. G. Drexler, "Predicting Later Articulation Abilities from Kindergarten Tests," *Journal of Speech and Hearing Disorders*, XXV (November 1960), 391-97.

Diagnosis

You now have the names of all candidates for your services and are ready to make your first diagnoses. Because you do not know how much time each case will take, you cannot set up a formal schedule but the teacher should be notified concerning the day and the approximate time. The pupils should come to the speech room singly. The upper-grade pupil can send the next classmate to you. The younger one, however, may need an escort. Perhaps the principal could assign a monitor to help you for a few days. If that cannot be done, you will have to call for the pupils yourself. Well, it's early in the year and you still have plenty of vigor to traverse those long corridors.

The speech room should be ready for work. The bulletin board should have a meaningful and attractive display. A diagnostic record sheet should be prepared for each pupil. In addition to the date and his name and grade, it has his birthdate, address, telephone number, and parents' or guardian's name. This latter information you should have previously obtained from either the speech records or from the central office. The testing materials should have been placed where they will be readily accessible to you, but not where they might catch the eyes of young children. Of the several good diagnostic tests on the market, you will have chosen the one you prefer or you will have compiled one of your own. Certain of the commercially prepared tests, such as Templin-Darley Screening and Diagnostic Test of Articulation * are excellent in their comprehensiveness. In the school situation, however, time is an ever-controlling factor and it is often expedient to use a less detailed test. Studies on the selection of materials and the methods used in testing have established reliable procedures. The work done at Indiana University (*182*) might serve as a guide in the preparation of your own test. Many therapists make their own cards and find that these are quite satisfactory. In addition to the diagnostic tests of all sounds in the three different positions and the rechecks of the questionable ones, you will want some time for unstructured conversation. It is the less formal responses that may give the most accurate examples of speech. Using a shorter test does not imply superficial evaluation. It means that diagnosis is a continuous process rather than an opened and closed activity. You will discover enough in the first day to start the therapy. Bit by bit in every meeting thereafter you will explore the complete speech pattern.

The tongue blades should be ready and the wastebasket handy because you will want to look at the child's speech apparatus. After checking the lips, tongue, and palate and noting the condition of the teeth, listen carefully to the nasal sounds. A few therapists prefer to postpone this examination until the child has had some experience in speech class. The audiometric test, too, should be given during the first meeting or shortly thereafter. Whenever you give this test make sure beforehand that the audiometer is ready for use. Questionable cases should be retested at another time. The results should be reported to both the health services and to the parents. The former should have a copy of the audiogram but the parents should receive a statement giving the date and saying, "Your child's hearing has been checked and found satisfactory," or "The results

* Bureau of Educational Research and Service, Extension Division, State Univeristy of Iowa, Iowa City, Iowa.

of the audiometric test indicate that your child has a possible hearing loss and should see an audiologist or otologist."

As a speech therapist you will work with a few pupils who have a hearing impairment which may affect their speech and their ability to hear all that is said, yet is so slight that placement in a special room is not recommended. If these pupils are doing work commensurate with their ability in the regular classroom, that is the place for them. They, however, can profit from what you have to offer. They can be taught speech reading, the younger the easier, and often they need to be made aware of their speech and of the particular sounds which may become weak.

You now have the basic information regarding the pupil: the school record, the speech diagnosis, the examination of the speech mechanism, the audiometric test, and possibly a psychological evaluation. You are ready to find a spot for him on the schedule.

6   Because schedule-making concerns the administrator, the teacher, and the
     pupil, what are the factors to be considered in each case?
     W. Johnson and others, *Speech Handicapped School Children* (New York:
     Harper & Row, Publishers, 1948), pp. 362-65.

Considerations in Scheduling

The screening is over and you may have a far greater number of cases (all of whom need you) than can be included in a reasonable load. If you are to visit several schools, determine the number of cases found in each and take this information to your supervisor or superintendent. Have that person help in making plans, but have some alternative ones to submit. Often by offering him two plans, either of which is acceptable to you, he can still exert his prerogative of choice.

You will need the class schedules from each school so you may note the recess and other break periods for every grade. To avoid conflicts and to assure the maximum use of room space, schedules for all itinerant teachers should be planned cooperatively. If the administration has not taken leadership in doing this, you might invite the other teachers who visit your schools to work with you on schedule planning. The administration, through building principals, supervisors, or superintendent, should participate in this meeting, but informal talks should be undertaken earlier with those concerned.

Begin your classes about ten minutes after school starts and end them five minutes before closing time, but schedule every other minute. The single greatest peril to the success of a speech program is a therapist lounging in the coffee room or sitting idly in the speech room. Enjoy your coffee, yes, but keep on your schedule and remember that an absent child does not mean an additional coffee break.

Coordination Day

As was reported earlier, a majority of therapists are given office or coordination time. Most commonly this is half a day a week. Although it is usually one complete afternoon, a few therapists prefer to take a short period each day and thus have some free time in every building. Ask your administrator's advice in selecting your office time. Friday afternoon is an advantageous one to use for this purpose. It is a time when classroom schedules are frequently broken for various assemblies, movies, and programs, and pupils are often not available for speech work. If several therapists work in a district, it is helpful for all of them to take the same day for office time, thereby making conferences possible.

Recognizing the exasperating warning embodied in Parkinson's Law,* "Work expands so as to fill all the time available for its completion," let us consider the utilization of the office time. What with lessons to plan, records to keep, and materials to be found, you are going to be hard put to allocate time in which to make the many contacts so much needed for an intellectually challenged therapist. Learn to arrange each day so the mechanics of the day-by-day teaching are cared for on the spot. For example, during the few minutes between classes, make your brief notes of what has been done and what you expect to do next. Before leaving at night put everything in its place. Before beginning in the morning, use the twenty minutes to prepare the materials for the day. The precious

* C. Northcote Parkinson, *Parkinson's Law* (Boston: Houghton Mifflin Company, 1957), p. 2.

minutes of the coordination half-day should be carefully husbanded and matters of first importance given first place.

If it is possible to do so, stagger your reports by doing some each week. This will make it unnecessary to write seventy-five letters at one time. Keeping these routine jobs and bookkeeping tasks up to date will leave time on your coordination day to make special examinations, to confer with parents, teachers and other personnel, to make home calls and classroom visits, to attend conferences, to locate new materials, and possibly, but scarcely probably, to do some professional reading.

Selection of Case Load

After getting the time schedule from the building principal, note recess and lunch periods. Then ask the teachers if they have certain periods that cannot be interrupted (usually the reading period). Note these for each grade. This is the framework within which you fit your schedule.

Now the selection of cases to be taken. Sort the diagnostic sheets according to grade placement. Study the tests and code each sheet to show its temporary classification: active (should be taken at once), referral (certain things must be done before he is ready for speech therapy), and waiting (probably can wait for a later assignment). Now take out the ones marked *active*. You will want to include all with marked organic problems and some from every other group. However, remember this! Do not take only those cases which appear to be the most severe. We are on very uncertain ground when we say this one will and that one won't respond to therapy. It is far wiser to take some cases from every age group and from every type of defect. Hopefully, you will hit a fair number of the less serious problems because these cases will improve rapidly and may be dismissed, thus making room for others. Don't stack your case load too heavily with slow moving cases as it is essential, also, that you show progress. In a measure you will be judged, fairly or not, by the number of cases that show obvious improvement. So it is necessary for a therapist, particularly a beginning one, to give himself a chance to win approval. Include a few children who have only *th* difficulties.

Since classroom teachers usually prefer to have all the speech pupils taken at the same time, try, when it is feasible, to put classmates into a single group. Count your groups and your individual-session people. Compare that number with the number of twenty-minute periods you have in the school. Study the groups with reference to room schedules. Too many groups and too many children? Something has to give. Take out those children whom you might put on the waiting list. The choice this time may be more on the basis of necessity rather than on the lack of urgency. Make some more rejections and try regrouping. Recess and reading periods may make it necessary to put the two left-over first-graders in with three second-graders. They are all articulation cases and have at least *s* and *r* problems in common. In the sixth grade is Dorothy who has been coming to speech for five years and still lisps. It might be wise to give her a vacation from speech for a year. Move those two sixth-graders into that morning period when the younger children are busy. Fred is seven and in the room for the mentally retarded. Yes, his speech is substandard, but so is everything else he does. He is just learning to be a member of his group. His teacher, with a low enrollment, works on his speech and language every day. You might give her some suggestions and materials, but do not include Fred in your case load this year. He is burdened enough trying to know one teacher.

So on until you have what appears to you to be a workable schedule. Take it to the principal for his suggestions. He may want to make some changes. Then go to each teacher and discuss it with her. Again there may be some changes, such as:

> Jane is weak in arithmetic and is scheduled for speech at that period. So you put her in a different group. Miss McKenna thinks Dorothy's lisp is cute—why bother? There are other youngsters with more serious problems.

Yes, you'll make some changes, but hold fast to the principle that you want some children from every type of defect. Do not accept the judgment of an untrained person as to which pupils need speech help. The principal or the teachers may have other valid reasons for not wanting a pupil in speech class at a certain time but the decision as to the speech need is yours. You may take out some names and put in some from the waiting list. This adjustment procedure is frequently a delicate one. Occasionally there will be a teacher who cannot find any time when a child may be taken from her room. You must show a willingness to make reasonable concessions, but be firm in the matter of the child's needing and getting speech therapy. A schedule, at least a temporary one, finally evolves.

The second group of diagnostic sheets are those marked referral. Who are these people? John was found to have a very severe loss in hearing. The nurse is arranging for medical attention and you suspect he will be placed in the room for the hard of hearing. Susie, a cleft-palate case, needs further medical care. You and the nurse are to have a conference next week. Billy and Izzy appeared to understand little of what you tried to do. After reviewing their cumulative records, you want to talk with their teacher and possibly the principal about getting psychological studies made. Helen burst into tears when you talked to her. The tale she told of her home life was rather sad. You have made a note to ask the social worker about her.

The problems presented by this referral group may lead you to a study of the community and its resources. (See section on Resources, pp. 49-101.)

Your waiting list is composed of those pupils whom you plan to take at the first opportunity. Teachers appreciate getting the names of their pupils who are on this list. This is an indication that they have not been overlooked. Later you will develop a fourth list, namely, those dismissed from therapy.

The Schedule

A schedule is now made. The principal gets a complete copy, and each teacher gets a copy of her section.

The first day or two you may have to call for the pupils, but after that have some other means for notifying them, such as these: when you arrive in a school, place an attractive poster reading SPEECH TODAY in a spot seen by all children, or make several smaller posters and have a monitor place one in each classroom, and then collect them at the end of the day.

The children leaving the speech class may notify the next ones. Often just opening a classroom door and nodding is sufficient. The

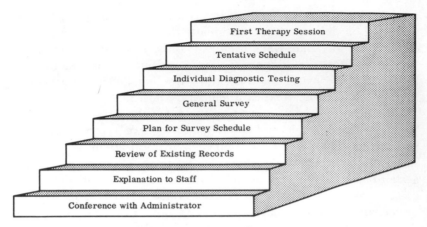

Figure 2. Steps in locating pupils.

children may be given clocks and calendars to put in their note-books. The classroom teacher, of course, has the speech schedule for her pupils and often she will remind them, but do not expect her to take this responsibility. She has too many other duties. In a few schools the principals have appointed monitors to bring the children to speech class. The truth, however, is that all known prac-tices fail at times and occasionally you will have to lope the corridors to call for some children. If forgetting becomes too consistent and you have tried every means of reminding the child, including a parent conference, then drop the name from your speech load. Notify the pupil, teacher, principal, and parent in writing of your decision and the reason for it. The next semester, try again.

After the over-all screening has been completed, the diagnostic tests evaluated, the case loads selected, the referrals instigated, the waiting list prepared, and finally, a therapy schedule established, you are ready to begin therapy.

HIGH SCHOOL PROGRAMS

The problems of screening and scheduling in high schools are basically the same as those in grade schools. You have to locate the students who have speech problems, diagnose them carefully, and then prepare the schedules. The organization within high schools, however, creates certain problems not found in grade schools.

Direct Identification Screening

The speech therapist takes advantage of the many methods of locating students with speech difficulties. Probably the most effective and most satisfying procedure is the direct screening of students by the therapist. In many high schools the practice of testing incoming freshmen through English classes has proved to be a workable means of reaching all ninth-graders. Some give freshmen screening tests during the time allotted to conference work so that testing will not interfere with schedules of speech therapy for upper classmen. On the other hand, some therapists find it advisable to postpone therapy until the testing of new students is completed. Others survey students during physical education examinations or during freshmen study periods.

In addition to the survey of freshman, the testing of all transfer students should be done soon after they enter school. Usually the administrator of admissions requires new students to visit the therapist for a test. In the interest of doing a thorough job of case finding, certain schools plan to screen all junior students as well as incoming freshmen.

Referrals

Because speech patterns vary from situation to situation, students may pass the screening test and still need help. Stutterers do not stutter in all situations. Hoarseness may be due to a cold. The therapist may have a momentary lapse of attention. For these reasons and others, staff members should be alert to the possibility of referral.

Other valuable referral sources are the speech therapists serving the elementary schools from which the high-school students have come. A plan should be developed whereby all past speech records are sent as a matter of routine to the high-school therapist for evaluation. Even though most children may have completed their speech therapy in the elementary grades, their original problems may recur upon entering high school. At any rate, all school reports should be examined carefully before further therapy is planned.

Survey and referral findings are recorded in a number of ways. Printed 5 x 7 forms which provide space for identifying information and for speech diagnosis and description are satisfactory for checking.

Name_*Kertz   Albert   Alden*_ Date of first interview _*9/17/62*_
       (last)   (first) (middle)

Home Room_____*217*_____ Study Periods _____*1 = 6*_____

Speech Schedule____*T = Th*____   *6 = 6*
                    (day)   (period)

Previous School_*Lincoln*_ Birthday_*6/7/47*_ Sex___*M*___ Class of___*'65*___

Parents or Guardian_*Alfred Kertz*_ Address_*2127 East St.*_ Phone_*7-9992*_

Diagnostic Findings: Comments:
Severity rating: 0 = O.K., 1 = mild,
2 = moderate, 3 = severe
                                              Voice high (2)
                                          No previous therapy

Yearly Summary of Work

A pencil should be used for recording home room number, study periods, speech schedule, address, and phone number.

Severe speech cases may profit from detailed studies which include all phases of the student's history.

Time Schedule

Ordinarily, high-school students are scheduled for two sessions per week. In some situations these sessions are the length of the regular school period and may include time for independent work in an adjacent therapy room. In other schools the students spend half of each of two study periods with the therapist and the remaining time in a study hall. Certain students, especially those working to achieve habitual production of a sound they have learned (this is called carryover), are seen once a week, depending upon need and schedule flexibility. As in all complicated programs, every teacher, including the therapist, will have to be cooperative. The student's welfare is the prime consideration.

By the time you have completed your testing and struggled through many revisions of your schedules, you may be tempted to relinquish your half-day of office time to take some seemingly desperate cases who cannot come at any other time. Don't. You will live to learn that more progress is made by serving fewer pupils well than by giving haphazard service to a greater number.

NEW DESIGNS FOR PROGRAM ORGANIZATION

We have discussed in some detail the most common type of organization for speech and hearing services in the public schools. There are places, however, where these plans are not practical. A widely scattered population, an insufficient number of therapists, inadequate housing facilities, a lack of funds, and sometimes even an incompetent local administration, are all reasons why other schemes must be devised. In various parts of the country more than a few people are trying interesting experiments in public school speech correction. We are including brief reviews of some of these.

A Rural Program *

The problem of bringing speech and hearing services to rural districts has always been a perplexing one. In some states the law permits county school boards to provide education for exceptional children through the office of the county superintendent of schools. In this situation a staff operating out of the county office may go to several small districts whose individual enrollments would not justify the employment of a specialized teacher. By the consolidation of their resources, the districts are able to employ not only the speech

* Reported by Richard Sweizbin (Multnomah County, Oregon) and Lloyd J. Thomas (Speech Correction Consultant, State Department of Education, Oregon).

therapist and other specialized teachers, but also an experienced director who can give leadership to the group.

The costs of such programs are met jointly by the state, the county, and the districts. While districts which are large enough to warrant the employment of full-time therapists continue in the traditional manner, the county plan is proving very successful in rural areas.

A Program for an Expanding Population *

Many school districts in urban areas are confronted with rapidly expanding populations, while both the supply of teachers and money remain fixed. How to use the speech therapist's talents most effectively and to provide the greatest service to children often present difficult problems. In one rapidly growing suburban area the following plan is being tried:

A school population of 7200 children in ten schools has two therapists. The state law requires an average case load of 100. The new plan gives speech services to all grades, kindergarten through twelve. One therapist has a case load of 150 first- and second-graders, treated in fairly large groups, and she provides speech improvement to the kindergartens. The other therapist serves grades three through twelve with a case load of 50 and provides the lower mentally handicapped classes with speech improvement. Thus the state requirement for an average of 100 cases per teacher is met.

The first therapist has a background in speech improvement and experience in working with large groups. Although speech improvement is given to all kindergarteners, only those first- and second-grade youngsters who have severe problems are given correction. If a problem persists until the third grade, the second therapist takes over. These cases need the intensive speech therapy which is possible with the lower case load.

In evaluating this program, the following advantages are noted: The therapists are able to utilize their best abilities and talents and to provide consultative services. More community agencies are utilized and the majority of the children receive adequate therapy relative to their problems. A major disadvantage is that much more

* Reported by Joan Weir, Public School Therapist, Portage, Mich.

traveling is involved and scheduling becomes a bigger headache than usual. Another difficulty is that the teacher-therapist relationship is diminished somewhat because the time in each school is considerably lessened. Because the program is new, an evaluation of its true effectiveness is not yet possible.

A Part-Time Central Clinic Program *

The lack of opportunities to consult with fellow therapists, as well as with other specialists, has long plagued field workers in our profession. Various plans have been tried in an effort to meet this problem. One program which employs six therapists varies the traditional twice-a-week schedule by having two half-days devoted to "clinical" work. The clinic is held in a centrally located building where the nurses, psychologists, remedial reading teachers, and the director of special education have their offices. This arrangement makes consultations fairly easy. Therapists with advanced training and experience usually staff the clinic. Younger ones, too, however, are given opportunities to participate in the work. Depending on the number of referrals, two to four therapists form the staff.

Severe and baffling cases are referred to the clinic. Some will be seen only in the clinic while others get the clinical service in addition to their twice-a-week lessons. The parents are responsible for bringing in the children. This practice makes frequent parental conferences possible and gives the parents a chance, when it is deemed advisable, to observe therapy. Surprisingly, little difficulty has been reported in getting parents to come.

Another advantage of this system is that grouping of cases with like problems has been made easier. For example, five adolescent stutterers from four widely scattered schools were brought together for group therapy. The therapists believe that the more concentrated therapy, as well as the consultations with parents and with other professional workers, has increased the effectiveness of the work. Another factor not to be overlooked in assessing the reasons for the success of a central clinic is the prestige associated with "going to the main office" for therapy.

* Reported by Alice E. Bonnette, Public School Therapist, Kenosha, Wis.

*A Pilot Study Comparing the Block System
and the Intermittent System of Scheduling
Speech Correction in Public Schools* *

The basic purpose of this study was to contrast the effectiveness
of the block system (daily therapy for several weeks) with the intermittent system. It was hypothesized that children with articulation
problems receiving speech correction under the block system make
a significantly greater gain in speech than a contrast group of children receiving speech correction under the intermittent system of
scheduling.

The experimental group was selected from a school population
of 1700 children enrolled in five of the eighteen elementary schools,
and was served by two therapists using the block system. The contrast group was selected from a school population of 3400 children
enrolled in the remaining thirteen elementary schools. These children were served by four therapists using the intermittent system.
In both the experimental and contrast groups there were approximately comparable proportions of rural and urban; Negro and
white; and upper, middle, and lower class children. Only children
of normal intelligence who had articulation problems were included. The Templin-Darley Articulation Test was given before
and after therapy. The results of these tests were used in determining an adjusted Barker-England Score. Additional information
was gathered in regard to group IQ scores, grade placement, age,
sex, and previous years of speech therapy. Following a typological
rating system developed at the University of Illinois, children were
assigned to one of four classifications according to the severity of the
articulation problem, the first classification representing the least
severity, the fourth classification, the most.

The schools on the block system were each allotted three blocks
of time throughout the school year. Each block extended for a five
week period. When the school was on the scheduled block, speech
services were provided four days a week for the five week period.
When the school was not on the scheduled block, speech services

* Reported by J. Weaver, Speech Therapist, and Janet P. Wol-
lersheim, Psychologist, Public Schools, Champaign, Ill.

were provided one day per week. Hence, while the school was on the block, a child receiving speech services under the block system would normally see the speech therapist each day for four days per week. When the school was not on the block, the child might see the speech therapist one day per week according to her judgment of the child's need for therapy. The speech therapist working under the intermittent system would normally see each child twice a week until the end of the school year and/or until the time of dismissal from therapy.

Under the block system the speech therapist had a continuous case load of from 35 to 40 cases per week for each five week block. His cumulative yearly case load was between 80 and 100. Under the intermittent system, the speech therapist had a continuous case load of 80 to 100 cases per week while his cumulative yearly case load was between 80 and 100.

When the total group on the block system was contrasted with the total group on the intermittent system, the speech gains evidenced by the children on the block system were consistently and significantly greater than those evidenced by the children on the intermittent system (5 per cent and 1 per cent levels of confidence). This was felt to be of considerable importance since the average minutes of speech therapy received for the school year was less for the children on the block system than for the children on the intermittent system. The difference in the minutes of speech therapy received was significant at the 1 per cent level of confidence.

When the children under the two systems were contrasted as individual severity groupings, the difference in speech gains between the two systems of scheduling reached statistical significance mainly for severity group 3. Even though statistical significance was not reached for severity groups 1, 2, and 4, the children within these groups on the block system showed consistently greater speech gains than did the children in the same groups on the intermittent system.

The hypothesis that children with articulation problems receiving speech correction under the block system make significantly greater gains in speech than a contrast group of children under the intermittent system of scheduling received strong support from the data.

A criticism sometimes made of the block system, namely, that the classroom teachers do not like it, was not found in this experiment. On a questionnaire, both the principals and the teachers were uniform in their praise of this system of scheduling.

> 7   In what ways does the Rochester report differ from the Champaign study? How does one tend to confirm the other?
> R. J. Van Hattum, "Elementary School Speech Therapy," *Exceptional Children*, XXV (May 1959), 411-14.

Summer Speech Clinics

In many communities, the public schools offer speech work as part of a summer program. It is more common, however, for the private agencies, such as the National Society for Crippled Children and Adults, the United Cerebral Palsy Association, or the Elks to maintain these services. They sometimes take the form of summer camps, and activities other than speech are included. University speech departments, too, frequently have programs in which children with speech problems are kept in residence for periods of from four to eight weeks.

Summer camps for stutterers are growing in popularity. Some authorities believe that in addition to getting a child who stutters into a new environment, the concentrated work on his speech which the camp situation makes possible is the most efficient method for helping him.

Educators in many areas are beginning to realize that summer months need not be lost months. This is certainly true for speech therapy. Speech goes on whether school is in session or not.

> 8   What values do these authors find in concentrated speech therapy?
> J. N. Clancy and D. E. Morley, "Summer Speech and Hearing Programs," *Journal of Speech and Hearing Disorders*, XV (February 1950), 9-15.

Conclusion

The programs we have reviewed give you pictures of what is happening in widely scattered areas and under vastly different circumstances. Many procedures are quite common to all programs. This, of course, is to be expected because the correction of defective speech is the prime objective in each. You have learned, however, that it is possible to adjust organizational plans to meet local problems. One test of your professional competence and your intellectual flexibility will be your ability to view a situation, assess its possibilities, and design a program which will serve the greatest number of children in the best possible manner.

RECORDS AND REPORTS

Effective speech therapy is dependent to a great extent upon functional records and informative reports. Although good practice is not necessarily reflected by good record-keeping, there is natural interplay between knowing what one is doing and reporting well what one has done. You should be both a student and a critic of your past performance.

Many good workers, it is true, are impatient with the amount of time spent on case records, yet no one would dare eliminate it. You will observe that the importance of having an opportunity to write these notes and reports is recognized in the planning of speech schedules. You will never have enough time but you will have some.

9   How does a consideration of semantics improve reporting?
     Robert E. English and Harold S. Lillywhite, "A Semantic Approach to Clinical Reporting in Speech Pathology," *ASHA*, V (June 1963), 647-50.

There are several purposes for keeping records and reports. The paramount one, of course, is for the welfare of the pupil. Pertinent information concerning him is recorded. Objectives, together with therapeutic procedures and their results are noted, all to the one end, namely, that you, the therapist, may give increasingly effective service. A second purpose is for administrative efficiency. Since you must function within the framework of a school, it means that certain types of information which can come only from your records must be provided. For example, the building principal must have your schedule and must know your case load in terms of the number of children and the types of problems. The classroom teacher must have her own pupils' schedules and their progress reports. The supervisor of special education and, in turn, the superintendent of schools will want certain reports, chiefly statistical, in order to determine space and staff needs. Finally, the state will require reports

SPEECH SCHEDULE

TO:___*Miss Holowitz—5th Grade*___

The regular speech program will begin___*September 23*___.
The following children have been assigned to speech class at the times
scheduled below.

Name	Day and Time		Therapy
Henry Sampson	*M & W—10:30-10:50*		*Artic.*
Joe Walsh	"	"	"
Frieda Fritag	"	"	"
Wanda Cohen	"	*10:55-11:15*	*Stuttering*
Harold Howe	"	*11:35-11:55*	*Voice*
Lester Hernike	"	"	"

This sheet may be inserted in your plan book where it will be
available for a substitute.

Here, too, is a green card giving names and schedules. Would you
please put it on the bulletin board each Monday and Wednesday.

Sally Jones
Speech Therapist

on numbers and types of cases served. These routine and seemingly
humdrum requirements will ultimately mean more efficient use of
space, money, and time.

Another reason for records and reports is that they are needed for
group or team work. To contribute intelligently at a staff conference,
each member must know what each problem is all about. If the
history has been prepared by one who has eyes trained to see, ears
trained to hear, and the ability to report accurately to a mind
trained to evaluate and diagnose, then an image will emerge which

reveals the present needs and provides guidance to the planning of effective therapy.

Records are also needed for student teachers who may come to you from time to time, and for your successor. Much time will be saved if these people can pick up where you left off. The final reason for keeping careful records is that they furnish research workers with valuable information. It is from the organized evidence of what has happened that new knowledge can be developed.

So let us consider ways and means for making professionally adequate records and reports. Some examples have been cited previously; others are now offered. These may not be the best possible records and reports. They are merely ones which certain therapists have found useful.

Waiting List

Copies of your waiting list, together with explanatory comments, should be given each teacher. She will like to know why some children are not taken immediately.

Daily Plans and Records

You may want to keep a log sheet for each pupil, or a log sheet for each day. Some therapists prefer a lesson-plan book such as other teachers use.

DAILY LOG

Dates	Comments	Name	Eastward, Bruce
9/21/64	Auditory stimulation—continued rhythm instruments.		
	Change frequently. Was hurt in fight.		
9/23/64	Absent.		
9/29/64	Quarrel forgotten. Identified three instruments'		
	sounds. Depressing cheek helps eliminate lateral		
	emission.		

OR

Daily Log

Pupils' Names	Comments	Date _9/21/64_
Bruce Eastward	Auditory stimulation. Continued rhythm instruments. Attention short. Change frequently. Face scratched by Pat.	
Mary Cole	Continued auditory. Introduce speech helpers. Use clown pictures.	
Pat Ryan	Kicked and scratched other boys. Angry over use of drum. Had to carry him into nurse's office and let him cool off. Mother belligerent on phone. What now?	

Case Record

A good case record contains a sufficiency of pertinent facts. That means relatively minor problems may not require detailed histories. Printed 8″ x 5″ cards make adequate and functional records. The back of the card may be lined and used for further remarks.

Case History

A case history form should be constructed. This will ask for pertinent information concerning all phases of the student's development. The extent to which you explore each facet will be determined by the severity of the problem, your own philosophy, and the availability of resources. This record will be added to from time to time and will not be completed until the student is dismissed from therapy.

Progress Reports

Both parents and teachers like to know what is being accomplished in speech therapy. A report of this type gives exact information and making it is not a time-consuming job.

Speech Diagnostic Chart

Roseland, Illinois

Name _Cotton, Sarah_ Birthdate _1/4/55_
Address _270 Main St._ Phone _221-9019_
School _Washington_

Grade	1	2
Teacher	M.D.	J.J.

ARTICULATION: Difficulty _Severe–very consistent_

Consonants:

	i	m	f		i	m	f		i	m	f		i	m	f
p				k				s				r			
b				g				z				l			
m				ng				sh				h			
t				th				ch				w			
d				th				zh				wh			
n				f				j				y			
				v											

Consonant Blends:

Vowels:

STUTTERING: _None_

VOICE DISORDERS: _None_
Pitch
Volume
Rate
Rhythm
Quality

STRUCTURAL ANOMALIES _None_

HEARING _O.K._

PERIOD OF SPEECH TRAINING

School	Date Begun	Date Ended	Why Ended	Correctionist
Wash.	_9/61_	_Cont._		_S.C._
_"_	_9/62_	_6/63_	_Sp. O.K._	_S.C._

35

Speech Progress Report to Parents and Teachers

Name: _____Herbert Hansen_____

School: _____Windmore_____

Date: _____1/64_____

Day and Time of Lesson: _____T & Th. 1:30 PM_____

Sounds worked on_____s, z_____

Check list for work accomplished in speech class:

1.	Produces the sound	Sometimes	Yes	No
2.	Uses the sound in words	Sometimes	Yes	No
3.	Uses the sound in sentences	Sometimes	Yes	No
4.	Uses the sound in reading material	Sometimes	Yes	No
5.	Uses the sound in conversation	Sometimes	Yes	No
6.	Almost ready for dismissal	Sometimes	Yes	No
7.	Cooperates with speech teacher	Sometimes	Yes	No
8.	Works well with other children	Sometimes	Yes	No
9.	Seems to enjoy speech class	Sometimes	Yes	No
10.	Shows a desire to improve speech through own efforts	Sometimes	Yes	No
11.	Needs to practice assignments	Sometimes	Yes	No

Additional Comments:

Needs to be reminded. Signal is a raised finger.

We would appreciate hearing your suggestions or any questions you might have, and invite you to visit your child's speech class at your convenience.

Sally Coleman
Speech Therapist

A brief personal note to the teacher stating the reasons for dismissal strengthens professional relationships:

Dismissal Notice to Teacher

Dear Miss Harrington:

Saul Gordman will not be coming to speech class. His speech is fairly good and he appears to have lost interest. I'll check him again next fall.

Sally Lund
Speech Therapist

Suggestions for Notes to Parents

There will be times when you will want to send some information to the parents. If each one is to get the same notice, a mimeographed form will usually suffice. One therapist,* however, increased the responses from a previous 50 per cent to 90 per cent by writing the invitations for conferences in longhand. When it is possible to do so, you will find personal notes, even hastily written ones, bring better results than the most cleverly done mimeographed job.

LETTER CONCERNING ENROLLMENT IN NEW PROGRAM

Dear_____*Mrs. Willy*_____

As you know, the Rose Park Schools are offering speech correction services. This is a program to help children overcome speech problems. You will hear more about this at the first P.T.A. meeting.

In our survey we found that_____*Harriett*_____'s speech needed some correction. She has been scheduled for help on_____*Tuesday*_____and _____*Thursday*_____from_____*10:10*_____to_____*10:30*_____.

We want to have a conference with you and are now in the process of arranging dates on which we can see the mothers. It may be a few weeks before we can schedule your visit. In the meantime, if you wish to talk to us, please call EN 7-7443. We are reached most easily on Friday afternoon.

Sincerely,

Ann Ainsworth
Speech Therapist

* Mrs. Grace Patterson, Speech Correctionist, Public Schools, Marion, Ill.

INVITATION TO VISIT

Dear_____*Mrs. O'Neal*_____ Date_____*9/26/63*_____

As you know_____*Mary*_____has been receiving speech therapy. We would like to talk with you about the work. On Friday, October 10, several of the mothers are coming to school for conferences. Could we schedule you for 1:15 to 1:35? Kindly let us know.

Sincerely,

Sonia Watts
Speech Therapist

Reports to Administrators

According to the administrative procedures in your district, prepare monthly, quarterly, semiannual or annual statistical reports for your building principal, your supervisor, and your superintendent.

SPEECH THERAPY MONTHLY REPORT

Date_____*Jan. 31, 1964*_____

Number enrolled at beginning of month	*92*
Number dismissed during month	*7*
Number added during month	*5*
TOTAL enrolled at end of month	*90*

Additional information:

Parent conferences	*4*
Parent phone calls	*12*
Parent visitations	*1*
Professional meetings	*2*
Other (*Talked at Lincoln P.T.A.*)	*1*

Henry Holloway
Speech Therapist

ANNUAL REPORT TO SUPERINTENDENT AND PRINCIPALS
ROSE PARK DIST. #10

Speech Therapist_____*George Puff*_____

Data for Year Ending June 19 *64*

Total number of students having received speech this year	*125*
Number of students dismissed with acceptable speech	*90*
Number of students dismissed for other reasons	*5*
Number of students retained for work next year	*30*
Average Monthly Case Load	*82*
Average Times Students Were Seen Each Week	*2*
Average Time for Each Class	*20 min.*
Total Enrollment of School District	*1374*

Classification of Speech Load

	Boys	Girls	Total
Articulatory	*61*	*40*	*101*
Phonatory (Voice)	*3*	*1*	*4*
Postoperative, Cleft Palate, Cleft Lip	*1*	*1*	*2*
Delayed Speech	*3*	*3*	*6*
Stuttering	*4*	*2*	*6*
Aphasia	—	—	—
Hard-of-Hearing—Lip Reading	*2*	*1*	*3*
Foreign Speech	*2*	*1*	*3*
Cerebral Palsy	—	—	—
TOTAL	*76*	*49*	*125*

Conclusions

There are no exact rules or perfect examples that will serve all speech therapy programs. Each of you will have to design the forms and reports which are best suited to your particular situation and write the accounts and letters which your personal philosophy and training dictate. There are, of course, certain guidelines. All records should be simple, accurate, and to the point. They should be prepared with the thought of the person who is to use them in mind. Will this give the required information? All accounts and letters should be scrutinized for their effect on the reader. Have I made the picture clear as I see it? Is the tone both professional and friendly? How would I react if I were to receive this letter or read this account?

And above all else, will this record, account, or letter contribute to better therapy for the child? This is the final and most important question. It is the one by which you judge the value of all your paper work.

ROOMS AND EQUIPMENT

Rooms

An adequate speech program is dependent in part upon facilities and equipment. You can give maximum service only if you have room to work with small groups as well as individuals, the needed tools and materials, and storage facilities which make efficient organization possible. While it is now rare to find a speech therapist working in a furnace room or a janitor's supply closet, in the early years these spots were frequently used. Nevertheless, since speech is a relatively recent addition to public school education, few buildings have rooms designed for the service. In a national survey 50 per cent of the therapists reported that their rooms were inadequate (72:15; Table 2-4). Another detailed study of one midwestern state found approximately 75 per cent of the speech rooms substandard (*173*). Your chances, therefore, of working in ideal surroundings are not too great.

You may have no choice in the location of a room, but if you do, pick a relatively quiet spot. Unless the room is sound-treated, avoid one that is next to a gymnasium or a band room where the bouncing of a hundred balls or the wails of a single maltreated violin will mar the beauty of your clear, undefiled s-s-s. The nearer a speech room is to the primary classrooms, the less time will be wasted between classes and the less you will be forced to participate in corridor problems, such as running, shoving, talking, loitering, and getting lost.

In an increasing number of situations, however, the new building programs give the therapists opportunities to work with the superintendents in making plans for speech rooms. You may be called upon to do so. These rooms may well be a part of a central suite

Figure 3. Multi-room speech clinic (Courtesy J. Sterling Morton High School, Berwyn, Illinois).

which includes a jointly shared waiting room and rooms for health, counseling, psychological services, and social work. With the alternate scheduling which occurs in smaller schools, certain itinerant personnel, such as the psychologist or the social worker, might share a room with the therapist. Health rooms, however, which are subject to frequent interruptions, make poor speech quarters. And avoid the teachers' rest room like the plague.

How big should a speech room be? In a grade school program where lessons will probably not exceed twenty minutes, a conference room which will accommodate a maximum of eight pupils will suffice. It is advantageous for you to have a small office in at least one of your schools, where the desk, phone, filing cabinet, and supplies are kept, thus leaving the larger room free for your therapy. If you are assigned one large room, screens or partial partitions can serve to separate the office from the therapy space.

The high-school program presents different spatial problems. Scheduling regulations may make it necessary for you to keep the students for a full sixty-minute period. Therefore, provision should be made for cubicles where speech may be practiced independently. Six, eight, or more students can be scheduled for the same period, some working with the therapist while others work independently. Flexibility is needed at this level.

Sound conditioning is of great importance. The extensive use of tape recording and the audiometric testing necessitate the use of acoustical tile or wallboard on the ceiling and cork or rubber tile on the floor.

In speech therapy we not only listen, we also look. The room should be attractively decorated and have adequate natural light and diffused artificial illumination of at least fifty foot-candles. This is the amount of light necessary for clear vision.

The following diagrams suggest plans which have been found efficient for both new buildings and remodeled ones as well as for both modest and lush budgets:

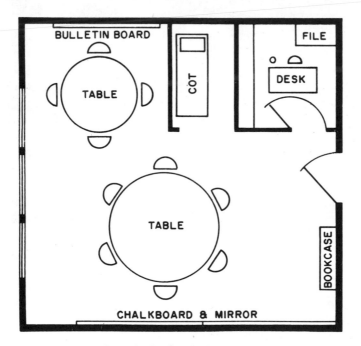

Figure 4. Grade school.

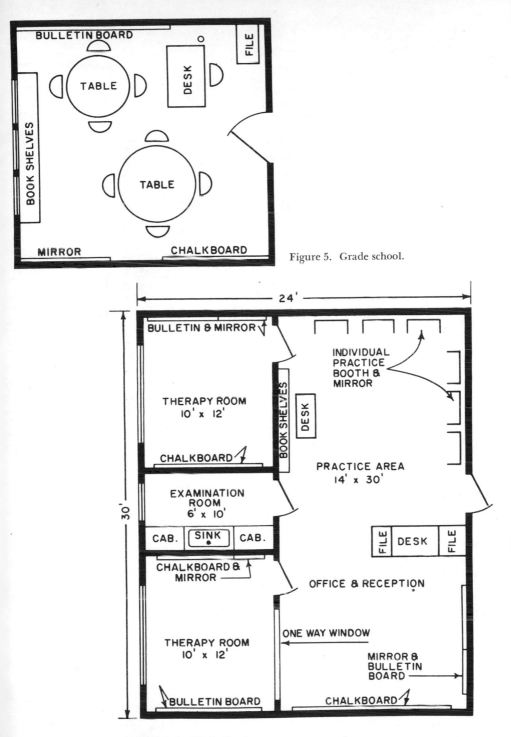

Figure 5. Grade school.

Figure 6. High school.

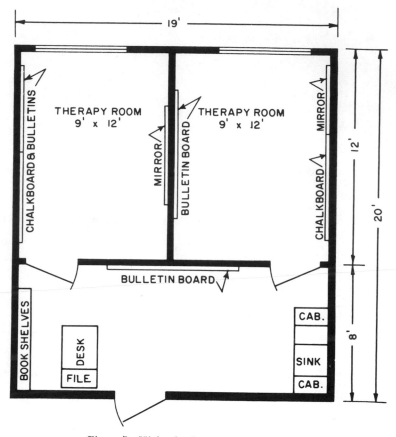

Figure 7. High school.

Equipment

A few items constitute the basic equipment for a speech room. There should be a table and chairs low enough so that the feet of the smallest kindergartener may rest comfortably on the floor and another table and chairs high enough so that the tallest adolescent may be seated with dignity. The teacher and the parent or school visitor should rate comfortable chairs. A desk equipped with a typewriter for the many reports and planned materials is standard equipment. A therapist with Freudian or Edna Hill Young orientation may want a cot for therapy, or she may need it for her own differential relaxation after the last small child lisps his way back to the classroom.

A filing cabinet that locks is an essential part of the equipment. Speech records must never be left where inquisitive eyes may read them. Shelves and cupboards are needed for the storage of books, games, charts, pictures, and small equipment, as well as for the audiometer, the binaural auditory trainer, the recorder and the record player.

A speech room would not be a speech room without a mirror. It may be of whatever size or shape you prefer. Some like the mirror fastened to the wall; others like it mounted in a movable frame with a bulletin board or chalkboard on the back. Or it may be hinged to the wall in such a manner that when it is swung one way the mirror is exposed, when swung the other, the bulletin board. (See picture page 100). In addition to the large mirror, pocket size mirrors and one of the magnifying type should be available.

The chalkboard is a time-honored aid to good teaching. Horace Mann himself is supposed to have said, "Indeed, in no state or country have I ever seen a good school without a blackboard or a successful teacher who did not use it frequently." Bulletin boards and feltboards, too, are aids that may be used to stimulate interest in a speech lesson. Many children, certainly those with halting tongues, need speech priming. "Tell me what you did over the weekend," is an ambiguous and frustrating request. Contrast that as a speech provoking technique with "The little boy in this picture is Tom. What shall we call his dog? Where are they playing? What do you thing is going to happen?" Speech will come because few and far between are the children who can resist thinking and talking about a boy and his dog. Or place on the bulletin board a cartoon which spotlights a topic of current interest to teen-agers. They will laugh and talk about it.

Instructional Materials

Tape recorders

are usually regarded as essential equipment in all speech programs. They have passed the novelty stage and their functional value as teaching tools is appreciated. The double track tapes make possible repeated comparisons of the student's speech with that of the model.

Auditory trainers

are many and of great variety. A pasteboard tube, a rubber tube attached to a funnel, a milk carton cut to fit the mouth and ear, or even an empty tissue box all make usable instruments for amplifying the voice and making it easier for the ear to detect slight differences. Group auditory training units such as are used in classes for the hard of hearing have been found useful in working with speech problems. Earphones, too, can be used to magnify sound. There are machines, such as the Language Master, which are designed primarily to teach speech; picture or word cards can be fed into these machines in order to teach vocabulary. There are other machines in which a light flashes when the correct response is given. A stethoscope, which can be purchased cheaply at an army surplus store or borrowed from the school nurse, can be used to detect glottal stop or nasal emission in the cleft palate child, lateral emission of a defective sibilant, the vocal fry in the child with a strident voice or in a stutterer's strained phonation. A toy plastic space helmet will improve self hearing and listening. There are on the market "talk-back" toy telephones (Gerber Co., Fremont, Michigan) which are unusually effective in enabling the child to scan and monitor his own utterance. One of the most effective new aids is the *binaural auditory trainer* which feeds the child's speech into one ear and the therapist's model into the other, thus permitting simultaneous comparison and the detection of differences in the two outputs. All these tools serve to emphasize the control hearing has over speech production and the importance of cultivating auditory awareness.

A reproducer

is needed for the growing number of records designed for speech work, as well as the great number of recordings which have been made of the world's best speech and music. If the school has one readily available to you, it may suffice. It is, however, convenient to have one which is kept in the speech room.

There are various situations in which you may use the reproducer. Boisterous, distractible youngsters may be quieted by having them listen for a few minutes to soft music. The many excellent recordings of teaching exercises may be used both to present new sounds and to reinforce those already taught.

Music,

both vocal and instrumental, is not being used to a great extent in our country. Europeans, however, seem to take more advantage of it in speech correction. If you have a bit of musical interest or talent, why not try? Pianos for speech rooms are usually not too difficult to secure. Some people give them away. Bells, whistles, toy xylophones, and bongo drums are all helpful in developing sound discrimination and rhythm. They should be a part of your equipment.

Visual aids

such as slide and movie projectors are needed in your work. These aids, which are increasing in number every year, are excellent in helping to solve the carryover problem. The child may be taught to think the good sound that is pictured on the screen, use it in self-talk, talk along with the picture character, anticipate what is coming next, and comment on what has been seen and heard. He may follow the pictures with voiced or whispered comments or he may use pantomime and silently think the correct sound.

A pure-tone audiometer

is essential equipment in every speech room. Borrowed ones are never available when they are needed.

Games

are loved by children of all ages. Speech therapists have used (and perhaps at times abused) this interest to reinforce their teaching. You, undoubtedly, have several interesting games ready for use in your model clinic. It must be remembered, however, that the game is only a means to an end and unless the end result can be defended, the game of itself has no place in a speech lesson.

10   What criteria do these therapists suggest for the judging of games?
      M. E. Black and R. A. S. Ludwig, "Analysis of the Games Technic,"
      Journal of Speech and Hearing Disorders, XXI (June 1956), 183-87.

Conclusions

Although you may have a carefully selected caseload, an efficient schedule, and well planned quarters, furnished with the best of modern equipment, they will all be dead timber unless you have a background of learning which provides the basis for the therapy, are able to utilize all environmental facilities, and are creative enough to add life and sparkle to the lesson.

In the final analysis, it is the therapist who teaches. More and more schools are providing good rooms and equipment; university centers are increasing in numbers and developing more extensive preparation programs; but it's your caring for and identifying with the troubled child that really get results. After looking over an elaborately equipped clinic, a master speech therapist said, "All you need are these," and he pointed to his head, his eyes, his ears, and his heart.

The School Administrator

SPEECH CORRECTION HAD ITS BIRTH IN THE SPEECH, PSYCHOLOGY, AND English departments of universities. Its early growth was nurtured by agencies devoted to child welfare, by interested members of the medical and psychological professions, and by organizations concerned with problems of childhood. Speech correction, however, blossomed into maturity when school administrators recognized how essential these services could be to the educational growth of the youngsters. Only then did our profession begin to grow. In those states where public school people have taken the leadership in securing favorable legislation, the programs have flourished and

2 *professional relationships, resources, and therapy*

grown with phenomenal speed. There are still a few states where speech services were not so sponsored. In these places charitable agencies such as the Junior League, the Elks, Women's Clubs, and others have promoted the work, but the progress has been very slow. Remember this if you decide to go into a state that is just now preparing new laws to sponsor speech correction. The most effective support both in getting the legislation and later in developing the programs has always come from the school administrators. It may be your responsibility to interpret speech correction to these people. If they are vitally concerned, action will start. If they are not, it will lag.

Putting speech therapy into the schools seems logical because it is there that all of America's children can be reached. Schools are everywhere and open to everyone. Private facilities can help only a few of those who need service, and therapy is then expensive. We   *49*

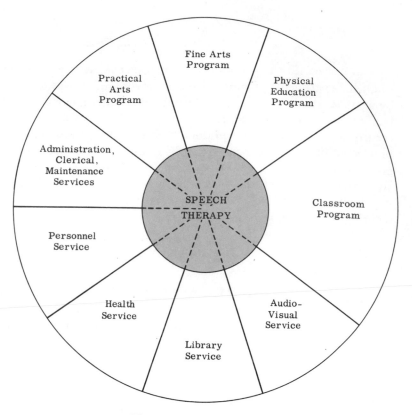

Figure 8. School resources.

must recognize that only through public funds can every child be served.

School is also a natural place in which to do speech therapy. Here is where most teaching is done. Children leave their classrooms for such activities as health checkups, remedial work, or individual tests; so leaving the classroom to go to speech is an acceptable procedure. The therapist even looks like a teacher—no white coat is worn. The room looks much like other school rooms—not like a hospital. And not the least in importance, school speech therapy is not initiated by the child's parents, nor are they paying directly for it. Speech correction is a school service and, as such, it may be accepted without any danger of losing status. A child can go to public school speech therapy without shame or anxiety.

A speech program in a school is like a plant in the fresh air. The air engulfs the plant completely and furnishes certain needed elements for growth. The plant utilizes these elements and returns to the air other equally important ones. In somewhat the same manner a speech program may absorb much that is vital from its environment and in turn give a service that will benefit the entire school.

By its very nature the school abounds in materials, information, situations, and professionally trained personnel, all of which may be utilized in speech work. Effective rehabilitative planning attempts to mobilize these resources to help the child with a problem. Let us look at the school.

> 11   What are the particular kinds of skills and knowledge needed by a public school speech therapist?
> Margaret H. Powers, "What Makes an Effective Public School Speech Therapist?" *Journal of Speech and Hearing Disorders,* XXI (December 1956), 461-67.

The Classroom Teacher

You will find that the classroom teacher's attitude toward speech correction will be the single most important factor in the acceptance of the service. Her attitude will be passed on to her pupils and they in turn will carry it home to their parents. She is the person in the most strategic position to reinforce your work. She can create situations in which the pupils may practice their newly acquired speech and, under her tactful guidance, experience the joy of accomplishment. Her attitude and her cooperation may mean the difference between success or failure. There may be a few crabbed old ones you can't win over, but in the main you will find that most teachers are sincerely interested in their pupils. You will need these friends.

How can you get acquainted with the classroom teacher? Meetings are usually held on the first day of school. Administrative and organizational problems are discussed and you may be asked to tell about the plan for the speech program. Of course, you cannot attend meetings in all buildings but, hopefully, you will soon be asked by each principal to meet with his teachers. If an invitation is not forthcoming, tactfully suggest that you would welcome such an opportunity. This meeting is your chance to get some needed information on local practices and to give a general picture of the speech program as you give the teachers the referral blanks (see page 9) to help you locate your cases. Later there will be other opportunities to confer with the teacher regarding particular pupils.

A conference regarding six year old Ida, who has a severe problem in articulation, might run something like this:

Speech Therapist: Ida was in with the other two little girls this morning. Sometimes I wonder if we are making progress with her speech. She appears to do quite well in auditory discrimination and can often repeat a sound and a word correctly, but the next week she is back to "an" for "man" and "all" for "ball."

Miss Jones: She is certainly an immature child in every way, yet she is improving. Just this morning I noticed she was able to put on her boots, coat, and cap about as fast as any child. Last fall she could not get into a sweater. During the "show and tell" period she stood before the class and recited "Peter, Peter" and the children understood her. Of course, she had a large picture of a pumpkin.

Speech Therapist: She's an only child, isn't she?

Miss Jones: Yes, and her mother works, so Ida is with Granny a good share of the time. I'm afraid Granny enjoys keeping her a baby.

Speech Therapist: I did talk with the mother early in the year but perhaps I should meet Granny.

Miss Jones: That might be a good idea. I'll send her a special invitation to come to P.T.A. next week and suggest that she visit the speech room.

Speech Therapist: Thanks. I'll be looking for her.

While much of the exchange of information with the classroom teacher will be done in an informal manner, it is often wise to have a somewhat structured basis for your counseling. To insure clarity and understanding, you may want your suggestions to be written. Copies should be given to both the principal and the teacher. Such a record might be something like the following:

RECORD OF CONFERENCE

Date:_____*10/1/64*_____   Name:_____*Brown, Helen*_____

Name of Contact:____*Miss Henry*____   Type of Conference:____*T. and S.T.*

Therapist:_____*I. Johnson*_____

Helen has a loss of hearing in her left ear. She is under medical care.

Suggestions:

1. *She should have a seat near the front of the room and on the left side, so her better ear will be near the teacher and toward the class.*
2. *When it is necessary for her to hear, she should be encouraged to turn in her seat and look at the speaker.*
3. *Any sign of unusual fatigue or inattentiveness should be reported to the nurse.*
4. *Attached is a copy of suggestions to teachers who have hard of hearing pupils.*
5. *Speech assignments will be in Helen's notebook. Please ask her to show it to you.*

Observing the Classroom Teacher

Since your case load will doubtless include pupils from all grades, you will need to vary your procedures to meet the interests and abilities of all age levels. Visiting classrooms and observing teachers at work will be one of the best ways to pick up ideas of how to improve your own therapy sessions. Plans for these occasional visits should be made beforehand with the principal and the teacher. Always remember that in the building with you there are specialists in all levels of child development. Some are master teachers from whom you can learn much. A visit to one of their classrooms will give you not only the requested opportunity to observe the speech of your pupil and to compare it with that of his peers but it will also make it possible for you to observe the art of teaching children at various age levels. Express your appreciation of her skill. A classroom teacher who has taught you something which you have used in your speech work will thereafter have a vested interest in your success.

One therapist made the following report on her visit to a classroom:

> During my visit to the first grade I observed Miss McClue using workbooks to develop auditory discrimination. The books had pictures of commonly known articles whose first and last sounds were alike, such as pan and pear, or boy and toy. I found other pictures of the same objects, mounted them on cards and used them to reinforce what the classroom teacher had taught. The children who came to me naturally were the ones in the group who needed this additional teaching. They were made proud and happy by the success they experienced in an activity which when first encountered had been difficult.

> 12 What suggestions in the literature on teaching reading may be utilized in speech therapy?
>
> E. C. Ronnei, *Learning to Look and Listen* (New York: Bureau of Publications, Columbia University Teachers College, 1951).
>
> A. S. Artley, *Your Child Learns to Read* (Chicago: Scott, Foresman & Co., 1953), pp. 102-9.
>
> M. Monroe, *Growing Into Reading* (Chicago: Scott, Foresman & Co., 1951), pp. 110-40.
>
> D. H. Russell, *Reading Aids Through the Grades* (New York: Bureau of Publications, Columbia University Teachers College, 1957), pp. 1-29.

Another therapist got this idea from a visit to a sixth-grade social science class:

> The class was studying transportation in the city and was using local maps. The three lisping children in speech class worked on a project called "Sight Seeing in Our City on Bicycles." They worked on directions for getting from one spot to another. The person correctly using the greatest number of *s* sounds won a new bicycle (picture).

The "Show and Tell" time in the first grade affords endless opportunities to use the newly acquired speech. Here is an example:

> Karen had difficulty with the *l* sound. She brought a doll to school which she named Lola and after careful preparation in speech class, Karen made the following talk during "Show and Tell." "This is my dolly. Her name is Lola. Do you know what she likes? Lemonade (picture) and lollypops (the real article). I love Lola."

The Classroom Teacher Observes You

The classroom teacher in turn will want to observe you at work. In all likelihood she never has watched a speech correction class in action and is curious about what happens. Through arrangements with the principal, she should be invited to make an occasional visit to see work with various types of speech problems. You will have the opportunity to show how speech correction differs from classroom teaching and at the same time to reveal many procedures common to both. While as a therapist you work primarily with a single pupil and his unique speech problem, both you and the classroom teacher share many methods.

Here is a demonstration given before a third-grade classroom teacher:

S.T.:   As you know, Miss Gale, Tom and Jim have been working on the *r* and Gottlieb on the *th*. We are going to play some of a recording we made of their speech last September and then you may contrast that with their speech today. Jim had a little *th* trouble then but it has disappeared.

(*The recording of each boy's speech is heard and each reads the same lines.*)

S.T.:   Note that Tom usually gets a good *r* at the beginning and middle of the words. He still has some trouble with endings. We need a little more work here. Jim's *r* is very good in the therapy situation but we wonder if he is always careful. Have you noticed his *r* in class or on the playground? You haven't? Well, suppose Jim comes to speech class for another two weeks and during that time will you notice his speech and then tell us what you think?

Gottlieb made fine progress in softening his *s* but the *th* is so very unfamiliar to him that he is taking a little longer to get it; nevertheless he is making progress.

(*A list of contrasting words is on the board: won/run, wed/red, wide/ride, car/caw, war/wall, dare/dell.*)

Tom and Jim, will you copy these pairs of words? Write sentences, each using a pair, and practice them every night after you brush your teeth. Watch your lips in the mirror. Let's look in our hand mirrors. *Won.* Note the slight puckering of the lips for the *w* sound. Now note the slight drawing back of the corners on the *r* in *run.*

S.T.: Gottlieb, here are ten *th* words. For your next lesson, test them and then underline the ones which have a voiced *th*. Practice saying the words three times every day. You might plan to do this right after you eat. Let's look at this pair: *thank/this.* Which has the voiced *th?* Yes, *this*—so underline it.

Our time is over. Thank you, Miss Gale, for visiting our class. May I come into your room sometime next week and hear the boys read?

Speech Improvement Classes

Speech improvement is generally recognized as the responsibility primarily of the classroom teacher. In a nationwide study *(46)* this was the consensus. It is an important part of the total language arts program. You, of course, have a genuine concern for its effective-

> 13 What are a classroom teacher's speech responsibilities?
> Elise Hahn, "Speech Defects Are Every Teacher's Responsibility," *NEA Journal,* XLVII (January 1958), 39.
> Nancy E. Wood, "Identifying Speech Disorders in the Classroom," *School Life* (U. S. Department of Health, Education, and Welfare), XLV, No. 5 (March 1963), 6-8.

ness because the better this program is the better will be the speech of all children and the fewer will be the minor articulation problems. This reduction in load will result in your having more time to devote to the complicated speech problems.

> 14 Compare and contrast the opinions of these authors concerning the responsibilities of a speech therapist for a speech improvement program.
> Verna Breinholt, "The New Look in Speech Education," *Exceptional Children,* XXII (February 1956), 194.
> Kathleen Pendergast, "Speech Improvement and Speech Therapy in the Elementary School," *ASHA,* V (March 1963), 548-49.
> Morton J. Gordon, "Third Grade Television Classroom Articulation Program," *Journal of Speech and Hearing Disorders,* XXV (November 1960), 398-404.

Your contribution to the speech improvement program will be the help you can give the teacher through lending her materials, discussing their uses, and possibly teaching an occasional demonstration lesson. There will also be times when you will survey the entire grade and then give your findings to the teacher.

> 15   How may the suggestions offered in this series of articles be given to the classroom teachers?
> Milton C. Eastman, "Speech Correction in the Classroom," *Grade Teacher*, LXVII (January 1950), 50; (February 1950), 48; (June 1950), 54.

The Principal

The principal is the coordinator of activities within a school building. Consequently the speech program, as far as administrative problems are concerned, is under his jurisdiction. He is the authority and is responsible for all that goes on. You will work with him on matters relative to your room, its furnishings, and its upkeep. Requests for supplies and mimeographing services will go to him. Your schedule, schedules of the pupils, problems with parents, or problems involving the relationships of the speech program to the school are all concerns of his. For example, any all-school notice or general letter should be approved by him before it is sent out, and if you are unable to keep your schedule, his office should be notified immediately. Periodically he should receive reports on your program (see pages 38-39).

In most schools teachers receive letters or bulletins which give general policies and directions. Study these and file them for future reference.

> A young therapist failed to read one of these notices and did not know the deadline date for the medical report on her chest X-ray. She was late, consequently, in submitting the results, and her first pay check was delayed for two weeks.

You will learn that the principal, with his knowledge of the school and its patrons, can be of great assistance to you in avoiding some pitfalls and in solving many problems. He is, however, a very busy person and should not be bothered with every little question. When you do ask for a conference with him, go with a list of topics to be discussed. He will appreciate this thoughtfulness.

Teachers' Meetings

While the fact that you serve several schools makes it impossible for you to attend every faculty meeting in every building, you will want to be at those which are related to your work and in which you can both contribute and learn. Very early in the year, possibly the first week, there will be an opportunity for you to explain briefly to the staff the plan for operating the speech program. Later, in all likelihood, you will be invited to discuss speech correction in greater detail.

To be of assistance in speech work, the classroom teacher should know something about it. Fortunately, more and more colleges are including some speech courses as part of the curriculum. Teachers, therefore, are becoming acquainted with speech problems and what can be done to solve them.

It is not safe to assume, however, that all teachers have some knowledge of speech correction. Interpretation is a continuous process. We have mentioned the exchange of visits with the classroom teacher as well as talks and demonstrations at teachers' meetings. Then, too, there are therapists who believe that interest in speech may be created by issuing bulletins periodically on such subjects as articulation, auditory training, stuttering, etc. In addition to these opportunities, there will be times when you attend the staffings of cases.

Recognizing the value of pooling the information various persons have concerning a child, schools are taking time to bring these people together for an informal exchange of ideas from which emerges a plan designed to meet the child's needs. These conferences are called staffings.

Staff Conference *

Participants:

         Director of Special Education
         Speech Therapist
         Classroom Teacher
         School Nurse
         Teacher of Mentally Handicapped
         Principal
         Psychologist

* Reported by Herbert K. Lotz, School Psychologist, Galesburg, Illinois.

The speech therapist had asked for a staffing on John, age 12 years, 3 months. The boy had been in speech for a year and a half and had made no progress. Nearly all consonants were incorrect or omitted, and he frequently used a glottal stop. He appeared to have almost no auditory discrimination for his own speech or the speech of others. When he occasionally could master a sound such as *f*, he could not carry it over to *fan*. The therapist questioned the value of continued speech work with him. She had a long waiting list.

The nurse reported a home call. The family was living on public welfare in a house which had heat in only one room. There was a problem of frozen water pipes and everything was dirty. The father was "sickly." Both parents were illiterate and they were uncertain as to whether they had 16 or 18 children. There was some argument concerning John's age. The parents reported a daughter as being 12 years old, but said the children were not twins.

Efforts to secure records from an out-of-state school proved fruitless. The school had burned.

The nurse had found 20/40 vision and the eyes turned out (wall-eyed). A local doctor had offered to correct this condition, but the mother refused to have the work done.

The teacher of a mixed third and fourth grade reported that John was three years older than anyone else in the class. He was a happy boy and loved to play games. The other children liked him. He was strong. He had made, however, little academic progress. Although he appeared to try, his work was at about the second-grade level. The principal, who had recently administered a group achievement test, noted that John had worked hard on it but accomplished very little.

In an extensive report, the psychologist found John a friendly child who entered upon the testing situation without seeming fearful. His speech was difficult to understand at times. He seemed to be fairly well oriented as to time and place and to pertinent data concerning his environment. The "wall-eyed" condition occurred only once. His cooperation and effort were very good throughout the test and he actually seemed to enjoy the opportunity. Of course, children perceive some of these tasks as games. His small muscle control was rather poor. This was noticed in using a pencil and manipulating small objects.

The psychologist went on to report as follows: According to the intelligence tests, this boy is functioning within the borderline defective range in verbal situations and as a moderately retarded child in nonverbal areas. This alone might account for his not profiting from work in speech. His learning abilities are limited. One of his greatest strengths is his ability to provide adequate definitions to vocabulary words. In this area he functioned as an average ten-year-old child. This is the type of child who may carry on a fairly good general conversation, which may be misleading, i.e., his comprehensional vocabulary is good and yet when it comes to reasoning, he falls short. He reasons on a very concrete level. He is also fairly good at verbally expressing good social judgment. Here he functions as an average nine-and-one-half-year-old child. In a hypothetical problem involving a social situation, he generally will know what to do. In reasoning and forming verbal concepts on a more abstract level, he functions below an average eight-year-old youngster. This would be reflected in his lack of progress in both speech and the regular school subjects. He would not be able to relate knowledge from one situation to another. He may learn a sound in the speech room but it just won't carry over to everyday speech. His ability to generalize is certainly limited.

One of this boy's outstanding weaknesses is his very inadequate fund of general information. John's attention span for rote material perceived auditorially is quite good. He should be able to profit from phonics in reading. He retains some sounds fairly well but he can't apply them in speech because this is relating and that is where he has his difficulty. His attention span for visual material is quite short.

The auditory method definitely would be the best in a learning situation. Nonverbally, this boy's visual perceptual and organizational skills in general are quite impaired. He has a great deal of difficulty in seeing the relationships of individual pieces even in very simple puzzles.

The speech therapist and classroom teacher said their observations agreed with the psychologist's findings. The psychologist made these additional comments:

John's visual discriminatory ability in areas dealing with geometric shapes and symbols is rather severely impaired. When attempting to reproduce geometric shapes with a pencil, he has considerable difficulty in making angles, etc. His reproductions are generally quite distorted. This impaired visual discriminatory ability is probably contributing to his reading problem. He is not always able to distinguish one word from another when they are similar in configuration. Intellectually, he is capable of doing beginning third-grade academic work, but he may not be able to achieve at this level because of his impaired visual perceptual skills. On an achievement test he reads words orally at mid-first-grade level. In looking at the word *big,* he says dog. *How* he pronounces *cow.* When he has additional picture clues, he is able to read for comprehension at a mid-second-grade level.

In number work John is able to do some additions with carrying, but knows only the very basic subtraction facts. This is about an upper-second-grade level. All in all, he seems to be underachieving for his indicated capacity. Much of this is due to his impaired visual perceptual skills.

Emotionally, there is no serious problem. He seems to be a fairly well-adjusted youngster and his emotional needs seem to be fulfilled from within his home, even though it is as bad as it is. He seems to have a good relationship with his entire family. The parents do not pressure this boy at all, nor do they punish him unjustly. John realizes that he needs help in school. This is one good thing in his favor and probably he will do better in the special classroom where he will be able to gain some success. He probably would function within the middle to upper third of such a group.

The principal discussed the placement with the teacher of the special room. The psychologist suggested that she use techniques designed for the brain-injured and that the teaching of phonics should be stressed. It was decided to discontinue speech until the boy was well-established in the new program. The nurse was to follow up on the sight problem and endeavor once again to get medical care.

Intelligent contributions to these discussions will do much to establish a favorable attitude toward our profession. The author has heard more commendation of speech therapists for their helpful participation in staff conferences than for any other single activity. Superintendents, supervisors, and psychologists frequently say, "The speech therapist more than anyone else present had a clear insight into the child's problems and made workable suggestions for meeting them."

Records and Guidance

One of the first of your office days should be devoted to becoming acquainted with the guidance department, or lacking that, the cumulative records file. You will want to learn what system for pupil assessment is used and what people are responsible for it. Usually you will find this information either in the main office or in the guidance department. In a few schools all records are sent to the child's classroom. In addition to academic records, the cumulative folder contains the results of psychological tests, the health data, and comments on social adjustment. Only after you are familiar with the information already available should you plan your own case histories. You will need all the help you can get from what is known about the child.

Familiarity with the cumulative folder will save you not only needless work but may prevent some embarrassment.

Mr. Johnson, a very thorough new therapist, was about to launch a campaign to discover why Ada had a hearing loss. The letter to the mother was written, but before he sent it, he remembered the cumulative file. He studied it and found a record of the child's school attendance, scores on group tests, and her academic grades, but no mention of health. Inquiry revealed that in this school all health records were kept in the nurse's office. Here he discovered a long medical history. Ada suffered from some allergy which periodically caused a respiratory difficulty. This sometimes resulted in a temporary loss of hearing. She was under the constant care of a well-known otologist. The letter to the mother was not sent.

The Guidance Staff

Depending upon the size of the school and the services offered, the guidance staff may consist of the following people: those directly responsible for educational planning, the psychologists, the social workers, the visiting teachers, the truant officer, the nurses and other medical personnel. Teachers concerned with remedial work also may well be of assistance to you in counseling with students who have severe educational problems.

The nurse's

awareness of the great need for assistance from a professionally trained worker who could direct stumbling tongues into smoother patterns has often furnished the impetus for creating a speech program. With a collection of statistical data concerning hearing losses, problems related to cleft palates and cerebral palsy, and failures or absences due to the inability to communicate, the nurse was often the person who convinced the school administrator that the employment of a speech therapist could be well justified. So it may be possible that it is to the nurse you owe your job. Cultivate her.

Whatever the reasons may be for the initiation of the speech program, you will profit from a very close working relationship with the health department. In most schools it is here that you will find each child's medical records and the results of all his physical tests. Seek them out. The nurse is often the person who has made home calls and knows the families. Frequently she is aware of a problem long before a child is enrolled in school. You will find that the best source of historical facts will be the nurse.

In addition to furnishing you with background information, the nurse will be the person to whom you refer all medical problems.

It is she who will make the arrangements for medical care, do the follow-up work and report to you the doctor's findings and recommendations. There may be times when you and she will wish to consider this a shared task. When this is the case, be very careful that each of you understands the exact extent of her own responsibility.

In many school systems the nurse is a full-time member of the staff and devotes all her efforts to the problems of children. In other school systems, however, she may be a member of a city, district, or county organization and give only part of her time to the schools.

One of your first contacts in the fall should be the nurse, and from her you should learn the administrative pattern in which she works and the extent of the health services. Your need for information in in order to compile a Local Resources Directory will furnish a good reason for visiting the nurse.

Psychologists

are available in many school systems to do testing and studying. In the early days, however, speech therapists had to be prepared to do their own psychological work. It is true, of course, that all therapists have fairly extensive background preparation in psychology and many have graduate work in this discipline, yet the lack of a wide testing experience, together with the all important time factor, makes it imperative that we seek the highly professional guidance which may be received from a qualified psychologist.

The chief function of the school psychologist is individual child study. When a child is referred to him, he studies facts already known about the child's history and present status, uses various techniques and evaluative instruments to study the child's learning ability, achievement, personality, special abilities and disabilities. He then analyzes and integrates the information gathered, participates in a conference where he and other members of the school staff present their data and make plans for helping the child, and writes a report which includes a summary of significant facts and recommendations. He re-evaluates and makes further recommendations when necessary. In some cases he participates in the treatment of the child's difficulties through counseling the child and the parents or through other specialized techniques. In all that he does he cooperates closely with other school personnel and often with professional persons or agencies outside the school.

> 16 What help can you get in knowing pupil personnel services and the techniques of referral by reading the following:
> Mary Alice White and M. W. Harris, *The School Psychologist* (New York: Harper & Row, Publishers, 1961), pp. 252-70 and 329-42.

Good psychological studies may help you in planning therapy for youngsters who are unusually slow in developing speech; those who are reluctant to talk because of overwhelming shyness; those who are moody, belligerent, or fearful; those who stutter; and those who appear to be functioning either markedly above or below their chronological ages. You will find that these deviant ones will need help. In systems having psychologists on the staffs, this presents no problem. Many of you, however, will have to look outside the school system for help.

Social workers

are employed in a variety of settings. Among the ones with whom the speech therapist will have contact are the psychiatric social worker in a child guidance clinic, the medical social worker in a medical clinic, the family case worker in a family service agency, the group workers in settlement houses or community centers, child-welfare workers from private and public child-care agencies, and the school social workers.

> 17 Describe briefly the school social worker and the methods used in social work.
> Opal Boston, "School Social Services," *Social Work Year Book* (New York: National Association of Social Workers, 1960), pp. 517-23.
> Helen Harris Perlman, *So You Want to Be a Social Worker* (New York: Harper & Row, Publishers, 1962), Chapter II, pp. 48-62.

Your Responsibility for Personal Judgment

While the contributions of the counselor, the social worker, the psychologist, or other specialists may assist you in knowing the student and may suggest plans which might help in solving his problems, so long as you are the one who is professionally responsible for his therapy, it is you who must chart the course. You need not blindly follow the findings or recommendations of other disciplines. They too may be wrong, although they are probably right. But this is your child, your responsibility.

It is often wise to investigate your own hunches and impressions, particularly when they differ from recorded findings. You too have had some excellent training in understanding human beings in trouble.

> Let us cite the case of Jim, enrolled in a class for the mentally retarded. He had an articulation problem which responded to therapy. During her sessions with him the therapist observed his lively interest in whatever she did. He just did not present the usual picture of a child with an IQ of 75. She studied the case folder and found that all the psychological tests consistently indicated he was retarded. His class work, however, had shown regular growth and achievement. Something must be wrong. It occurred to her to check his birth certificate. She found that an error had occurred in recording his birthdate on the psychological test. The boy, in fact, was two years younger than the chronological age listed on all of his records and, consequently, was of average intelligence. Admittedly, this is not a common occurrence but it illustrates the necessity for following your own judgment at times.

Cases involving a loss or a suspected loss of hearing should be checked and rechecked. Remember that the environmental factors, the accuracy or calibration of the audiometer, and the competence of the tester all contribute to the reliability of the test and that any one of them may distort the results.

> One therapist suddenly noticed that many of the pupils tested between ten and eleven o'clock on Tuesdays seemed to have unusually poor hearing. He observed carefully the extraneous noises which might disturb hearing and then realized that this was the hour jet planes took off from a not-too-distant airport. When the same children were tested before ten o'clock, their hearing losses were never as severe.

Materials and Experiences

Every grade level and every department from kindergarten through high school contain rich resources for therapeutic materials and experiences. Books from the library and the classroom, workbooks, and discarded books and magazines all furnish ideas for therapy. Science exhibits, such as charts on oral hygiene, art materials such as pictures and media for creating displays, songs and instruments from the music department, and equipment from the audiovisual department are among the many material resources which may be yours for the asking.

> 18   How can you utilize the suggestions made in this article?
>   A. T. Murphy and R. Fitz Simons, "Music Therapy for Speech Handicapped," *Elementary School Journal*, LIX (October 1958), 39-45.

The child with a speech problem spends most of his day in school. It is here where situations may be created in which he can learn to assume responsibility, experience leadership, and develop social poise. It is here where his physical development may be fostered and where he may learn to express himself through creative arts. All these experiences may make important contributions to the emerging personality and to the development of satisfactory oral expression. As a speech therapist, of course, your specific interest is the child's speech. The school furnishes endless opportunities for using newly acquired speech habits. Classroom procedures, extra-curricu-

> 19   What beneficial results came from this experiment?
>   Eileen Marquardt, "Carry-over with Speech Pals," *Journal of Speech and Hearing Disorders*, XXIV (May 1959), 154-57.

lar activities, class organizations, and playground experiences are among the situations which may be utilized by the resourceful therapist to create meaningful motivation for perfecting speech.

> 20   Speech therapists will be helped by knowing how to prepare materials such as puppets, dioramas, panoramas, and movies. Directions for making these things and discussion concerning the age levels of children interested in them may be found in the following:
>   Viktor Lowenfeld, *Your Child and His Art* (New York: The Macmillan Company, 1954), pp. 80-82, 98-99, 103.
>   C. D. Gaitskell, *Children and Their Art* (New York: Harcourt, Brace & World, Inc., 1958), pp. 266, 280, 359-61.

This is a very brief review of the opportunities for speech therapy offered in schools. There are none greater. The suggested references direct your attention toward readings in various areas. These should be thought provoking, but in the final analysis your professional competency will be determined by the degree to which you are capable of utilizing your knowledge in the alleviation of speech defects and in the development of a genuine empathy with children who have problems.

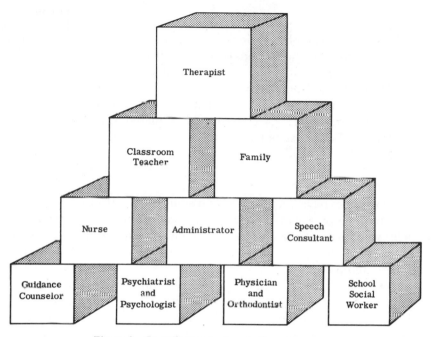

Figure 9. Contributors to speech therapy.

COMMUNITY RESOURCES

Professional Colleagues

We will consider the school therapist's relationships with certain other professional colleagues. Referral and consultation are extremely important in speech therapy at every level. No single worker can ever hope to possess all the skills and knowledge needed to resolve all speech problems. Children come to us with a host of difficulties which affect speech problems and their successful treatment. A hungry child does not learn easily. An anxious child cannot concentrate. There will always be some children with organic anomalies which must be minimized or stabilized. And even in your own field of therapy itself there will be need for the information and help which other speech therapists can provide.

Referral Relationships

In view of these observations, it is apparent that you must come to know the other professionals who can help you when your own resources appear inadequate. Who are these people? How can you locate them? And how should you proceed in making a referral? Much of your success will depend upon how well you can answer these vital questions. Circumstance has placed these children in your arms. You must not drop them. If you find it hard to hold them, get help.

State Agencies

Many states have boards or commissions which are clearing houses for information concerning organizations or individuals who can help you. Some of these agencies are government supported, others are maintained by private funds, some are national in their scope, others simply local or statewide. All, however, assist in establishing and improving child welfare services in communities, and whether it is state or national, private or public, each agency needs your help in locating the problems it is dedicated to relieve. In turn, each agency can at least give you certain information and guidance.

Among the state supported agencies are commissions which are the outgrowth of White House Conferences, commissions which are appointed by state governments, and divisions or committees within state departments of health, of welfare, or of public instruction.

To illustrate how one speech therapist used a state agency to help her with a cleft-palate child, we cite the following report:

Josie's parents were very poor and could not possibly afford the prosthesis I felt she needed. Indeed I wasn't sure that a prosthesis was what she did need, but I was determined she just had to have something better than the miserable speech I did not seem to be able to improve. She had been operated upon very early in life but there was no palatal movement, no uvula, nothing but a mass of scar tissue. The family doctor felt nothing further could be done. Somehow I just couldn't accept this. Josie had tried so hard for me. And so I first wrote to our county health nurse. She suggested that I contact the Division of Services for Crippled Children (sponsored by the state university). Here I learned that the application for medical help must be made by the child's parents through their family doctor to the local nurse who represented the Division. I called at the home and explained why I thought Josie could be helped by the type of specialized care the Division could furnish and told the parents how to get an appointment. Together the mother and I visited the doctor. He was very glad to cooperate in preparing the application for service. Once the Division nurse received this, she took over the case and made all the necessary plans for Josie to be referred to a cleft-palate team for evaluation and necessary care. I did no more until the Division wrote me saying the surgery had been done, the prosthesis fitted, and invited me to come to a staff meeting where the case would be reviewed and where I could consult with the speech therapist connected with the Division. This I did and there I received expert opinion on how I should proceed. To reinforce the work done during the school year, the Division sent Josie to its summer camp. Here for six weeks she received concentrated therapy in addition to having vacation fun far beyond anything she had known heretofore.

Occasionally during the next two years Josie and I returned to the clinic to demonstrate the progress we were making and to receive further suggestions. Today she is a happy high-school girl with reasonably good speech.

Private Agencies

There are many private agencies, both national and local, which are interested in serving children with certain diseases and disabilities. Of these, the National Society for Crippled Children and Adults and the United Cerebral Palsy Association are the most prominent. Here are two accounts of assistance given by agencies:

One agency participated in a research study on physical factors which might contribute to faulty articulation. This had been conducted cooperatively by a college and the public school program. Some provocative facts had been discovered. More statistical analysis was needed but the money was gone. The therapist presented the problem to the United Cerebral Palsy Association and received a grant of money which made possible the completion of the work.

Another example of the type of service given by private agencies is this:

In a county where no speech therapy services were available, the National Society for Crippled Children and Adults established a speech clinic. After it had been operating a year and had demonstrated the effectiveness of therapy, the schools established their own program. The clinic continued to operate, serving children not enrolled in public schools.

Local Agencies

This account shows how one therapist found a local mental health clinic helpful in working with a baffling case:

> Sam was a bright, likeable high-school boy who stuttered severely. As the therapist grew to know him, she found that he lived, at least partially, in a world of fantasy. He told tales of being the manager of a professional basketball team which traveled to distant parts of the country. He said he spent his weekends flying here and there. At first she thought he was kidding, but she soon recognized he was deadly serious. However, he did not reveal this private life to most people. Since the school had no psychologist and the therapist knew the boy needed far more help than she could give him, she turned to the local mental health clinic, which had both a psychologist and a psychiatrist on its staff. After talking first with the boy and then with his parents about the need for expert help with his speech problem, she persuaded him to ask for an appointment at the clinic. She also got permission from the parents to talk with the staff and to exchange information concerning the case. Following the initial contact, the clinic took over the treatment and the school therapist followed its suggestions. It took months of work with the psychiatrist before the boy began to distinguish between reality and fantasy and to forget his dream world. He gradually developed a fair degree of control over his speech and on the whole became a well adjusted high-school boy.

> 21   What assistance might you expect from a family service center?
>   Russell H. Kurtz, ed., *Social Work Year Book, 1960* (New York: National Association of Social Workers, 1960), pp. 251-57.

Service Clubs

Every community has service clubs and most of them are looking for worthwhile projects. Here is one therapist's report on how he provided an opportunity for the club to participate in helping handicapped children:

> When I arrived on my new job and checked on the equipment, I found I had inherited an audiometer which obviously had traveled many miles under many masters. After attempting to test the hearing of a few children, I knew my misgivings were justified. The machine worked only by spurts and the manufacturer said that further attempts to repair it were useless.

> The school administrator met my request for a new audiometer with the time-honored and possibly true answer, "Can't you make the old one

last another year? No provision has been made for an audiometer in the present budget."

I was disheartened. The children's need was now. Then, too, I was anxious to get the therapy program off to a good start and to demonstrate I was a first class therapist. What could I do?

In the late fall I received an invitation to talk at a local service club. An idea was born. I announced I would talk on hearing and its relationship to speech. At the appointed hour I arrived with the audiometer under my arm. I set it up where all might see its faded beauty. For twenty minutes I talked on the dependency of good speech upon good hearing and the medical reasons for the early detection of hearing losses. I described briefly the function of the audiometer and then offered to give a demonstration of its use. A man volunteered. For a few minutes the audiometer appeared to be working perfectly, but then there was a complete silence. I tinkered but nothing could revive it, so I explained our problem and said I feared the testing of the children's hearing would have to wait for a year. Almost immediately one member rose to his feet and said he thought the club could solve the problem. The school got a new audiometer and the local paper carried a picture of the club's president making the presentation. To accompany the picture I prepared an article describing our program.

The children were tested and with the usual perverseness of fate, not a single significant loss in hearing was found. The next fall, however, I discovered three cases that needed immediate medical attention; so all the efforts were justified.

The Family Physician

The family physician may prove to be either your colleague or possibly a subtle stumbling block. Much depends on how well he understands your work. The therapists in one city decided it would be wise to acquaint the medical people with the speech program. Through the superintendent of schools, an invitation was secured to talk at a monthly meeting of the medical society. After discussing briefly the program in general, the therapists showed a film on speech correction.

Following this the doctors were asked what information they wanted on the hearing and voice problems which would be referred to them. There was some discussion and then two doctors were appointed to draw up the forms. Plans were then made to have two meetings with the therapists, teachers of those with hearing losses, and the nurses. At one an otolaryngologist would talk on "A Healthy

Voice" and at another an otologist would talk on "The Detection of a Hearing Loss." At each of these conferences the therapists suggested that there were specific things they should know about the medical problems of certain speech cases and asked if forms could be sent with the patient for completion by the doctors. This was agreed upon, so together with well-prepared resumés of all three talks, samples of forms were sent to each doctor and to each concerned school person in the community. The channel was now cleared for a well-understood working relationship between the two groups.

Another therapist working alone in a small town where there was no medical organization accomplished much the same thing with each doctor by calling him and asking when it would be convenient for the therapist to come to the office and explain the new speech and hearing service. As a result of these visits a plan was made to meet the problem of having neither an otolaryngologist or an audiologist in the community. When the family doctor believed it was necessary to do so, the children were referred to the out-patient clinic of the medical school at the not-too-distant state university. If parents were unable to provide transportation, a local service club would undertake the responsibility.

If you approach medical people with an attitude of both respectful deference for their superior knowledge in their specialties and of honest confidence in your own knowledge of voice and speech problems, you will have no difficulty in establishing rapport. Most doctors will be very cooperative if they know something about your speech therapy services *before* they are confronted with a specific case. Make their acquaintance early.

22   How do you think the various problems suggested by these authors could be met by a young therapist?
Herold Lillywhite and Richard L. Sleeter, "Some Problems of Relationships between Speech and Hearing Specialists and Those in the Medical Profession," *ASHA*, I (December 1959), 127-31.

The Audiologist

An audiologist, as you know, is a professionally trained person who assesses and evaluates hearing. In some areas audiological services are available through the school districts. When this is the case, the hearing testing program will be the responsibility of that person and your task is to refer cases to him. Usually his background involves training in speech pathology so he can often also serve as a consultant. Find the one nearest you and establish a professional relationship.

> 23 What change in the point of view of the medical profession toward the nonmedical person whose skills in working with handicapping conditions as part of a team is evidenced in this book?
> Davis Hallowel and R. S. Silverman, eds., *Hearing and Deafness*, Rev. Ed. (New York: Holt, Rinehart & Winston, Inc., 1960), pp. 3-19.

The Otologist

The otologist, the otolaryngologist, and the rhinolaryngologist are medical specialists who come from the group of professionals once known as ear, nose, and throat specialists. They diagnose and give the needed medical treatment for diseases, pathologies, or organic deviations in these structures. Most of your hearing, voice, and cleft-palate cases should be referred to one of them, if this has not already been done.

> An example of a case that baffled the therapist was Helen, a dainty little doll, whose hoarse voice fitted poorly with the rest of her personality. Upon the suggestion of the therapist, the nurse had the parents take Helen to the family doctor. He found the laryngeal examination exceedingly difficult and referred her to an otolaryngologist. This man discovered nodules on the vocal folds and instituted remedial procedures. When he thought she was ready for voice training, he notified the school and Helen was scheduled for therapy sessions.

The urgency for immediate referral of suspected hearing losses is illustrated in this case:

> Wilbur, age 8, was noted by both his teacher and the therapist as growing increasingly inattentive. The audiometric test made six months previously had shown no hearing loss, but the therapist decided to give him a second one. This showed a marked loss in the left ear and a slight one in the right ear. A conference with the nurse revealed that Wilbur had had a brief but severe illness the past October. She contacted the mother who took him to the family doctor and to an otologist. Treatments followed which resulted in the restoration of the hearing to almost normal levels. The boy was then given a seat near the front of the room and where his best ear was pointed toward the teacher's desk. The therapist added some speech reading to his work with her and by the end of the year Wilbur was an attentive, wide-awake boy.

The Dentist and Orthodontist

The dentist and the orthodontist, who serve the occasional case which requires highly specialized work, are both people with whom you will have some contacts. A few school systems have dentists on their staffs, but most dentists work either privately or in clinics outside the schools. Many schools, however, have annual dental surveys. These occasions may give you opportunities to become acquainted with the dentists. Get to know them.

> 24   What effect may visceral swallowing have on the development of certain phonemes?
> Marion Minst Ward, Sister Helen Daniel Malone, Gladys Reid Jann, and Henry W. Jann, "Articulation Variations Associated with Visceral Swallowing and Malocclusion," *Journal of Speech and Hearing Disorders,* XXVI (November 1961), 334-41.

Because of the interest in the tongue thrust problems, the dental profession frequently asks the speech therapists to work with certain pupils. When a speech problem is present, you have a responsibility, of course. If there is no speech problem, you are not justified in using clinical time for service somewhat out of your field. We are speech therapists, not tongue trainers.

> 25   To what extent does the problem associated with tongue thrust affect speech therapy?
> Samuel G. Fletcher, Robert L. Casteel, and Doris P. Bradley, "Tongue Thrust, Swallowing, Speech Articulation and Age," *Journal of Speech and Hearing Disorders,* XXVI (August 1961), 201-8.

A Case for an Orthodontist

Tall, eleven-year-old Henry, called Bugs Bunny by most of the kids, had a slight frontal lisp. The therapist had not been working with him very long before she recognized that his speech defect was the least of his problems. The boy hated his protruding teeth and tried in every way to avoid calling attention to himself. In the classroom he refused to recite. On the playground he hung around the fringe of the crowd except in situations where his fists could command respect.

After getting acquainted with Henry, the therapist talked about the possibility of having his teeth braced. At first he was greatly interested, but when she indicated the possible cost, his face fell. "We couldn't afford that," he said. She then told him that there might be ways of getting assistance and would he mind if she talked with the school nurse. He was willing. Together the therapist and the nurse worked out a plan. The nurse knew a competent orthodontist who would do the work for the lowest possible amount. Through a home call, she found that the parents would be able to pay half of the bill. An application to the Student Welfare Fund secured the rest of the money. The work was started. The orthodontist's kindly, matter-of-fact confidence in the ultimate results and the morale-booster shots given Henry periodically by both the therapist and the nurse helped to keep up his spirits during the long months of wearing the braces. Toward the end of the period when speech therapy was resumed it was only a short time until Henry was able to speak in an acceptable manner, and by the time he entered high school he was elected vice-president of his class.

Once in a great while the needs of a particular child are such that you believe you are unable to meet them as adequately as could some other therapist. These are examples of such situations:

Craig was a hard-of-hearing boy who had been making a fairly good adjustment in his regular room and, therefore, had not been transferred to the special room which happened to be in the same building. The therapist, however, was not satisfied with the growth in either his speech or his speech reading. She believed her preparation in this work had been too scanty. On the other hand, the teacher in the room for the hard-of-hearing was an exceedingly well prepared person and, also, her case load that year was light. Arrangements were made to have Craig take his speech lessons from her instead of from the speech therapist. He made good progress under the new plan.

Eric, a thirteen year old boy with a repaired cleft palate, had worked for two years with Miss Dokol and had fairly adequate speech, but there was room for improvement. She felt, however, that she had tried everything she knew and was getting rather stale on the job. Eric on his part seemed weary of coming to the same old speech room. At about this time Miss Dokol learned of a new therapist who had just joined the staff of a nearby university clinic. This man's main interest was cleft palate speech and he was anxious to get cases. The transfer was made and Eric, thrilled not only with new surroundings but also by having a male therapist, took on a new interest in improving his speech. The results were happy ones for all concerned.

So after you have tried everything you know and still are not convinced that the best possible speech is being obtained, do not hesitate to turn to other speech therapists for help or consultation.

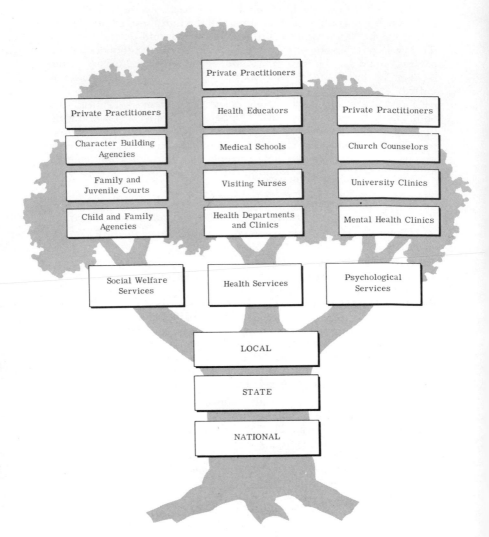

Figure 10.　Community resources.

How to Locate Referral Agencies and Individuals

A new therapist in a community should locate the available resources. The first places to look are in directories. There is one published each year by the school district. This will give you the names of staff members and their assignments. Next, locate a city directory or possibly one prepared by a council of social agencies. Here you will find listed the community services. Both the state and the national offices of education have directories. Copies of these may be found in your superintendent's office. And finally, you will want to consult the classified section of your telephone book. Check carefully, however, the professional status of persons listed there.

A second source of information will be your co-workers. Ask the guidance people, the special education personnel, the nurses, the administrators, psychologists, social workers, and the teachers about the services which may be secured both in and out of the schools and the procedures used in contacting the staffs.

Finally, you may want to write letters or make personal inquiries to national, state, and local agencies, clinics, or governmental departments whose functions are not clarified by your investigations. It is fairly safe to assume that there is some resource somewhere that can help you with any of your problems. Your job is to locate it. You will find that preparing a directory which indicates the type of service offered by each person or agency, as well as the address and telephone number, will be exceedingly helpful.

26 How do considerations which enter into the choosing of professional counseling guide your interviews with parents?
Lee E. Travis and D. W. Baruch, *Personal Problems of Everyday Life* (New York: Appleton-Century-Crofts, 1941), pp. 360-80.

How to Refer a Child

Frequently you will find established and routine procedures for referring a child to an agency or service, both inside and outside the school. These procedural patterns are as follows: A problem involving purely educational procedures goes first to the classroom teacher and then possibly to the principal or the elementary supervisor.

> You have discovered a young child who you suspect has a tendency toward reversals in his reading and you believe the remedial reading teacher should see him. The referral goes first to the classroom or homeroom teacher and then possibly to the principal or the elementary supervisor. Requests for psychological studies may follow the same channels, or you may refer a child directly. Reports on the progress of the case may be made directly to you or to you through the teacher.

All problems with possible physical causations are usually referred to the school nurse. In some schools, however, the nurse prefers to have the speech therapist process any medical referrals that concern speech or hearing problems. Whatever the procedure is, it should be clearly defined by the principal, or whoever is in charge, so there can be no misunderstanding between the nurse and the therapist. Each of you should keep the other informed of what has been done regarding the medical care of any speech case. If a child is to be taken out of the school building or if he is to see a medical person, written permission must be obtained from the parents. You can use a form such as this but accompany it with a letter or phone call.

ROSE PARK SCHOOL
Rose Park, Illinois

Date_____*11/4/63*_____

Permission is given for_____*Henry Hill*_____to be

taken to____*City Clinic*____ (or examined by Dr.____*J. J. Brown*____)

Signed_____

(Parent or Guardian)

Routine examinations given to all children do not require these permission slips. Nor is permission required when a child is given a psychological examination or enrolled in a speech class. These are normal educational procedures.

When there are family or social problems with which you need the help of the visiting teacher, guidance counselor, or social worker, you can probably contact and work with these people directly. Some school systems, however, have their own traditional procedures concerning the relationships between departments, so inquire about the routines to be followed. If these matters are processed haphazardly, you could render a real service by instigating a study which would result in an orderly plan for supplying information and service where it is needed and with the least possible amount of work. This could be a job for your second year.

Referral Letters

A good referral letter is one page in length and gives the identifying data, the problem involved, and your particular concern. More detailed information may be supplied after the case has been accepted and the worker indicates what he wants to know.

In reporting cases, two errors frequently occur. The first is incorrect or missing dates. The birthdate should be carefully checked and every letter or report should be dated. The second is statements of judgment instead of concrete examples of behavior. Instead of saying that a mother is irresponsible, write "The mother agreed to come for a conference on Tuesday but said she forgot about it and went to a movie instead."

27 What help can you get from Dr. Lee in writing professional letters? Irving A. Lee, *Language Habits in Human Affairs* (New York: Harper & Row, Publishers, 1941), pp. 115-51.

The following letter will give a social worker sufficient information to decide whether or not to accept the case.

January 10, 1964

Mr. Sam Gary,
School Social Worker
Washington School
Rose Park, Illinois

> Re: Suzie Jones
> Birthdate: April 7, 1955
> Address: 1719 5th St.
> Parents: John and Mable Jones
> School: Lincoln
> Home Room: 221

Dear Mr. Gary:

For the past four months I've been trying to correct a lisp in Suzie Jones' speech. Little or no progress has been made.

Suzie appears to have no interest in her speech. In fact, she shows little interest in anything. She sits, listless and indifferent, and stares out of the window. Group tests indicate that her ability is above average, but her class work is barely passing. She comes to school poorly dressed and not clean. Most of the time she he has had no breakfast. The usual school examinations have discovered no physical problem. She is rarely absent because of illness.

I made a home call and found the house in a turmoil. The baby was crying and the dogs barking. The father works regularly but the mother appears unable to handle money. I observed a color TV set and empty beer bottles. The mother complained about milk and shoes being too expensive for her to buy.

At this point in her life good speech is scarcely important to Suzie. She is hungry and cold. Could you give some help to this family? Both her teacher, Miss Ann Wendt, and I will be very glad to assist in any way we can. Mrs. Allison, the principal, knows the family and would like to talk with you.

My conference time is Friday afternoon but if that is not convenient I'd be glad to arrange for another time to come to see you.

Sincerely,

Ann Wilson,
Speech Therapist

cc: Mrs. Allison
    Miss Wendt

This letter shows why an occasional therapist fails to receive professional recognition:

January 10, 1964

Dr. H. H. Holmes
417 Fifth Street
Rose Park, Illinois

Dear Dr. Holmes:

Mrs. Johnson is bringing Judy to you to have her throat examined. Judy's hoarse voice shows she has nodules on the vocal folds. Will you please correct this condition.

Yours truly,

Henry Wolf
Speech Therapist

First of all, this referral should probably have been made by the nurse. If the therapist had to accept this responsibility, a copy of the letter should have been sent to the nurse. The letter itself is a very poor one. It not only fails to give identifying information, such as age, address, and the reason for concern, but it also offers a medical diagnosis which in itself is illegal. Finally, it orders the doctor to proceed with a cure. Don't ever write a letter like this.

In the following letter, the therapist refers directly to the psychologist, but as is indicated, the classroom teacher and the principal have been consulted.

April 10, 1963

Dr. Alice Waterman
Psychologist,
Rose Park Public Schools,
Rose Park, Illinois

> Re: Peter Constant
> Birthdate: 9/3/55
> Address: 77 Melby Street
> Parents: Sam and Ida Constant
> School: Lincoln
> Room: 201

Dear Dr. Waterman:

Peter has been receiving speech training for two years. Records indicate that he made slow progress the first year, but the past six months there has been no progress and possibly some regression. His speech is at the four-year-old level.

The health record shows no significant findings and the group psychological test places him in the dull-normal group. He is the youngest of three boys in what appears to be a good home. His class teacher, Miss Sandio, says he is not working up to capacity and may be retained in the second grade. Both she and I would like to know more about this child. Mrs. Allison, principal at Lincoln School, has suggested we write you. Could you see him? If so, we will send you copies of all the information we have.

Sincerely,

John Swanson
Speech Therapist

cc: Mrs. Allison
    Miss Sandio

If the psychologist agrees to make this study, then he should be furnished with copies or excerpts of all the information in the boy's school folder: attendance record, health history, placement on group tests (if the test itself is available, send a copy of it because his performance on certain items may be revealing), academic record, and reports on contacts with the home. The psychologist may have questions she wants you or the teacher to answer. Offer to come for an interview.

Many of your referrals will be to speech and hearing clinics:

ROSE PARK SCHOOL
Rose Park, Illinois

February 10, 1964

Dr. John Johnson
Speech and Hearing Clinic
City University,
Parkton, Illinois

Re: Henry Hertzel
Birthdate: 7/15/55
Address: 773 S. Main Street
Rose Park, Illinois
Parents: John and Sue Hertzel
School: Jefferson
Grade: Third

Dear Dr. Johnson:

Henry Hertzel is an eight-year-old boy with whom I have been working for two years and have known for four years. In the kindergarten survey I graded his speech as immature but did not make a complete diagnosis. I saw him again in February 1962 and checked his speech carefully. (See attached diagnostic sheet.) Since then he has come to speech class twice a week. Progress has been made in correcting the articulation, but he is rapidly developing into a stutterer. At first I thought he had only normal blocks and repetitions. In the last two months, however, he is beginning to blink his eyes and twitch his lips when he attempts to talk.

His teacher, too, has observed this and his mother has been in school twice to discuss this problem. (See attached reports.)

His health record, including hearing tests, is normal and on group psychological tests he ranks in the upper third of his class. He is doing above average school work. He has many friends and, as far as I can observe, he is a well-adjusted child.

I have never worked with a problem exactly like this and I need guidance. May he have an appointment at your clinic? His mother and I will bring him. The school will be very glad to furnish additional information if you want it.

Sincerely,

Sam Silversmith
Speech Therapist

A brief summary such as this tells the clinic enough so a decision can be made on whether or not the child should be brought in.

THERAPY

Let us consider the therapy session. This is the test of your preparation and your skill. Can you teach? More than good intentions and vague notions are needed to lead a child from the familiar to a mastery of the unfamiliar. Psychologically sound and skillfully executed plans are required. A competent therapist carefully determines the ultimate objective of the work with a student and then plans each activity so that it may contribute to that end. Playing by ear is for emergency situations only. In the long run it will contain too many misses for the few hits scored. How is such a therapy plan constructed?

Figure 11. Waiting for you.

Objectives and Criteria

To be effective, every speech therapy session should be directed toward specific objectives, and certain basic criteria should govern the selection of techniques and materials. The objectives for the students and those for the therapist may or may not be the same, and there will be immediate and long range goals. Let us give some examples of these different goals.

In a period devoted to critical listening, the therapist might be using the same activity primarily to quiet a distracted group and secondarily to develop the ability to listen, but the pupils would have as their objective the identifying of sounds made outside the school window. In preparing for a "show and tell" activity, the child might have as his objective the entertainment of his classmates, while the therapist would be using this highly motivated activity to strengthen a newly learned sound. A child's knowledge that he is preparing a speech to give before a class might make training in articulation more meaningful.

This is an example of individual work with a stutterer where different goals are evident:

Fred, a twelve-year-old boy, had a severe stutter. There were no children in school with whom a workable speech group could be organized, so Miss Haskins decided to take him alone. The ultimate objective, of course, for both the boy and the therapist, was to increase his speech fluency. The immediate goals for each, however, were not the same.

After joking with him a moment about the burst of speed she had seen him use in getting into the building when a sudden shower broke up the noon hour ball game, Miss Haskins went directly to the business of speech. (Few children appreciate pointless conversation. They know why they come to you.)

Explaining that she wanted to understand exactly what happened to him when he blocked in speech, she asked him to teach her to stutter the same way he did. They sat down in front of the mirror and went to work. This gave her a good opportunity to analyze his speech pattern— her main objective. Fred's immediate goal was to teach her to stutter as he did. In doing so he would analyze his own speech.

The period was finished by having Fred read a short paragraph for recording. He was interested in using the recorder, but he blocked several times. Miss Haskins suggested that during the next session they would study the recording and see if they could find any causes for the blocks in particular places, and also that she planned to stutter for him and he was to decide whether or not she had learned her lesson well. In the meantime would he please try saying "Good Morning" each day to at least three people whom he ordinarily ignored and then report their responses at the next session.

Here is an example of a voice therapy session in which the girls are not yet aware of any goals:

This was a second therapy session with three high-school girls. Their English teacher had referred them to speech because of unpleasant nasal voices. In the first diagnostic session it was evident that none of them was much interested in her voice and had come to speech simply because she had been scheduled to be there.

Mrs. Haas decided that her first objective was to awaken the girls to the fact that voices could be intriguing. She opened the session by saying, "This is going to be something of a fun-with-voice period. First, we are going to listen to a poem read by Helen Hayes, the great actress." She played the record of Hayes reading "Jabberwocky." *

"Now I'll read it as I might after a long, weary day." Mrs. Haas read the poem in a flat, monotonous voice. The girls giggled.

Mrs. Haas then played "The Children's Hour" and again she reread the poem, this time in a nasal voice, and again the girls laughed.

"There is a good bit of difference in voices, isn't there?" Miss Haas commented. "Some are much more pleasing than others, aren't they?"

"Well enough of that. Let's get acquainted with our own voices. You know that few of us really know what we sound like. Let's do some listening."

Each girl was given a milk carton which had an opening cut in it and was shown how to use it so that she might hear her own voice as others hear it. The girls then took seats in various parts of the room and proceeded to listen to their own voices while reading some sentences. After doing this for a short time and growing somewhat familiar with their voices, Mrs. Haas asked them to practice the sentence, "Do you see that man?" until they thought they were using their best voices. Recordings were made and the voice qualities were analyzed. This was followed by some work on an easy production of the word *home*.

It was fun and the objective of the session was accomplished. The girls were now somewhat conscious of voice, and what was more, they wanted to come back and see what would happen at the next session.

* Poet's Gold, RCA Victor, LM 1812.

The preceding examples illustrate the therapists' endeavors to bring about certain immediate objectives.

Now let us consider therapy in the light of certain other criteria. If it is group therapy, *will all the children be participating actively all the time?* There are many ways to include all of the children in an activity. While one child speaks, the others may be asked to listen critically and later give evaluations. When you ask a question, ask it, pause for a moment to give everyone a chance to formulate an answer, then call on one. Another method is to give checklists to pupils and ask them to make written records of the speech heard. At times some chorus work may be done. Pupils may work individually and continuously in various parts of the room, with the therapist moving from station to station, or they may work in pairs with one monitoring the other's speech. One therapist used advanced pupils or a normal speaking child to assist others who were having difficulty. She had prepared a checklist which the helper signed, and at the end of each period he evaluated his own performance. Some children learn best from their peers.

Is the activity *appropriate to the child's need?* Plans for group activities are simply bundles of individual plans. There may be connecting bands but the separate segments are the more important parts. Even when the children in the group have a common problem, one pupil is certain to progress at a different rate from the others. For example, four children may need help with *s*. Two may respond slowly to auditory stimulation and need extensive experience with this activity. Of the other two, one may master the *s* in all three positions as a single sound but may have real trouble with blends. The fourth may progress rapidly and at the end of two months be ready for dismissal. The therapy must obviously be planned with at least three different objectives even though the group is in general working to learn the standard *s* sound. When the members of a group have radically different problems, the attention given individual needs must be even greater, and of course the pupil's chronological age and achievement level are of prime consideration in planning therapy. Your own vocabulary should change from grade to grade. The primary children will be interested in what the Grey Goose says, the intermediate pupils in the sound *th,* but the high school students will feel more important if they are asked to consider the phoneme [θ].

The therapy session *must stimulate interest and be enjoyable.* Maintaining a high level of performance through weeks and sometimes months of repeated effort to establish a desirable speech pattern will challenge your ingenuity. Games may help. Children love them and can often get the speech reinforcement needed through the repeated responses which are integral parts of the game. Caution must be exercised, however, to prevent the winning of the game from being the prime objective and to focus attention and efforts in the production of good speech. By having the progress of the game depend upon clear speech, a functional value for it is established. Recognizing the brief periods allotted for therapy, we cannot afford to use games containing time-consuming activities which do not require speech. In making game selections we must also consider the age and interests of the children. Winning at some point must be possible for everyone involved, but this should happen only after genuine efforts to produce the best possible speech have been made.

Differences in personality needs must also enter into the planning for individuals. The restless child may learn best when given frequent opportunities to move about. The shy child may learn his first responses in a chorus situation. The aggressive child may do his best work when he is helping or checking someone else. Each activity must be planned to meet a particular pupil's need at a particular time.

> 28   How may the principles of motivation and learning discussed by the following authors apply to speech therapy?
> W. H. Burton, *The Guidance of Learning Activities* (New York: Appleton-Century-Crofts, 1952), pp. 4-12.
> Ralph L. Shelton, W. B. Arndt, and J. B. Miller, "Learning Principles and Teaching of Speech and Language," *Journal of Speech and Hearing Disorders,* XXVI (November 1961), 368-76.
> Gordon Low, Mildred Crerar, and Leon Lasser, "Communication Centered Speech Therapy," *Journal of Speech and Hearing Disorders,* XXIV (November 1959), 361-68.

The ultimate goal, of course, is the best speech the child can be helped to produce, but achieving that goal may take months or even years of practice. In the meantime, as we have indicated, intermediate or minimum goals should be established. These should be within the child's span of comprehension and memory. Not every defective sound should be attacked in the first session, or possibly not within the first several months. This experience demonstrates this point:

> Three shy second grade boys had lisps. In the first lesson the therapist had them greet her, saying "Good morning, how are you today?" No *s* sound was required. They worked for a clear greeting. This was followed by some work in distinguishing the *s* sound from *k* and *m*. The responses were in signals. No attempt was made to produce the sound. In the next session the auditory work was continued and the *s* sound was contrasted with *f* and *j*. This time the boys learned to recite "Peter, Peter, Pumpkin Eater," and were presented with yellow pumpkin badges. The following session *s* was contrasted with *sh* and *ch* and toothpicks were placed in the middle of the four front teeth. Practice was given in directing a thin stream of air along the toothpick. No comment was made on the sound produced.

So on. Although the maximum goal was to get a clear *s* in all speech, each session had a primary goal which could be achieved and which prepared the child for the next and more difficult step. Each day the child recognized that he had accomplished something. A new sound is mastered by progressive approximation.

> 29 The determination of goals in speech therapy is a necessary but sometimes difficult task. In an article "The Speech Defective Child," *Exceptional Children*, XX (November 1953), 56, Dr. Harold Westlake discusses this problem as it applies to various types of speech defects.

While the basic philosophy and many of the suggestions heretofore offered may be applied to high school as well as to the elementary school therapy, yet because of the physical and psychological changes occurring during adolescence, activities which appear more sophisticated are required, and effective therapy must be attuned to the mercurial variations in the needs of these fledgling adults.

> 30 Reviews of significant studies on adolescence will be found in:
> Raymond G. Kuhlen and Beatrice Lee, "Personality Characteristics and Social Acceptability in Adolescence," *Mental Hygiene*, Peter T. Huntras, ed. (Columbus, Ohio: Charles E. Merrill Book Co., Inc., 1961), pp. 227-44.

There are a few guiding principles to be remembered when selecting materials to be used with high-school students.

The work must have academic respectability. This is the best and possibly the only argument for giving grades and credit in speech work. Occasionally calling attention to the likenesses and differences between speech and academic work will help to underline the seriousness of speech work. For example, you might point out that most subjects are content subjects. They are studied to acquire new knowledge. Speech, however, is largely a matter of acquiring skill and can be refined only by repeated reinforcement; hence one must work at it constantly. There is no standing still. One goes either forward or backward.

The work must be made to appear adult and must be associated with things the adolescent looks upon with favor. For example, activities patterned from athletics, driver training, typing, music, or TV are popular.

> 31   How do high school age students regard their peers? What does this mean in planning speech therapy?
> Caroline B. Zachry, "Changing Personal Relationships," *Emotions and Conduct in Adolescence* (New York: Appleton-Century-Crofts, 1940), pp. 346-418.
> To what extent do the following authors confirm what Dr. Zachry has said?
> Lee Travis and D. W. Baruch, *Personal Problems of Everyday Life* (New York: Appleton-Century-Crofts, 1941), pp. 194-225.

You will be wise to appeal to the student's feeling of "I want to do it because it will be important to me and because there are people I respect who can do it." Once you win him on that basis, you have him. This is why it is important that you be an outstanding member of the faculty. This is why it is necessary to have school leaders who are enthusiastic about speech included in every group. Adolescents follow the stars. It is wise to focus attention upon the importance of good speech to popular and successful persons. Study TV and radio programs as well as recordings for beautiful and effective speech.

Can the goals for each child be kept in mind? Here is where case histories, records, and lesson plans are important. No busy therapist can possibly remember all details and plans concerning every case. Brief written lesson plans kept open on your desk will serve to refresh your memory. Keep a pencil in hand to jot down an idea as it pops. That, plus an occasional review of the child's complete record, will keep your therapy pointed toward desired objectives.

Mere repetition for the sake of repetition will not establish new speech patterns. The learning of speech, as for all learning, results from the student recognizing a need. When good speech makes it possible for him to manipulate his environment, then he will acquire good speech. The mechanics of producing a sound often have to be taught in isolation, but as soon as the production has been mastered the sound must be put in a word and that word used in speech which has immediate communicative significance.

> 32   What criteria have these authors established for judging a good therapy
>   session?
>   C. Van Riper and John Irwin, *Voice and Articulation* (Englewood Cliffs,
>   N. J.: Prentice-Hall, Inc., 1958), pp. 100-104.

When the reward for good speech consists primarily in getting an opportunity to spin a spinner and move a counter, the child's motivating objective becomes winning the game. The carryover of the new speech thus acquired into real life situations may be very slight. When a glow of self-pride, however, is the result of an increased control of his environment, the child is anxious to repeat this heart-warming experience. A little recognition of speech improvement, such as a smile or a wink, will let the child know you are aware of what he is doing. Asking a child to deliver a message to the janitor is a subtle compliment. One arthritic therapist, whose room was in the basement, always sent an extremely shy little girl to the principal's office on the second floor to say, "Miss Gochal says 'Good Morning.' " The child had an experience in social conversation and the therapist's presence in the building was announced. The class bully may get the recognition he longs for when he learns that good speech gives him the opportunity to issue the commands for a speech therapy game. The shy child may grow in self-confidence and vocal strength when she is "May Queen" and has to call her subjects to the throne to receive flowers and compliments for their good work. For young children who have been learning to produce a *th*, a stabilization might be achieved by playing a toss-ball game where the commands, "Throw the ball" or "Don't throw the ball" determine the activity.

33   Contrast the major differences in teaching an s sound by the following
      authors:
      O. Bachus and J. Beasley, *Speech Therapy with Children* (New York:
      Houghton-Mifflin Co., 1951), pp. 118-29.
      C. Van Riper, *Speech Correction: Principles and Methods* (Englewood
      Cliffs, N. J.: Prentice-Hall, Inc., 1963), pp. 242-70.
      R. West, J. Ansberry, and A. Carr, *The Rehabilitation of Speech* (New
      York: Harper & Row, Publishers, 1957), pp. 371-84.
      E. H. Young and S. S. Hawk, *Moto-Kinesthetic Speech Training* (Stan-
      ford, Calif.: Stanford University Press, 1955), pp. 19-21.

In another situation a toy figure of a little boy marching along
the picture-lined street which has been constructed on the table may
give many opportunities for comments on *s* words such as street,
sidewalk, gas station, postoffice, house, stop sign, policeman, and
school. Two or more toy figures will induce some conversation.
There will be, of course, remarks which contain no direct reinforcement for the *s,* but that is not bad. The important fact is that you
have created a situation in which children participate in normal,
interesting conversation. It is true that the stimuli for producing
an *s* are numerous and that you quietly correct a "bad" *s* sound, but
from the child's standpoint he is a boy walking down the street and
making comments on what he sees.

34   Why does Dr. Hahn stress communication as an important part of the
      therapy session?
      Elise Hahn, "Communication in the Therapy Session: A Point of View,"
      Journal of Speech and Hearing Disorders, XXV (February 1960), 18-23.

Is some *psychotherapy* provided? In an inconspicuous place on the
desk of a great teacher was a framed copy of this little prayer: "Dear
God, please help me to remember that this child, too, is an individual." That might well be the constant prayer of all therapists.
It is never the lisp you are treating; it is always the person. The lisp
just happens to be the particular condition that brings this child
to you, the person who has the specialized knowledge and understanding needed. But in each therapy session you must seek to
make the child a stronger, more self-respecting personality. The
first essentials in providing good psychotherapy (and we speak of it
gingerly and not psychiatrically) are your genuine concern for
people and your faith, built on sound preparation and thorough
study, that you can help alleviate most speech problems. If these

two factors are absent no readings can give them to you. You would better seek employment outside the speech profession if you have no faith or concern.

35 What toys and equipment are suggested for speech play therapy and where may one learn more about the techniques used in role-playing? A. T. Murphy and R. M. Fitz Simons, *Stuttering and Personality Dynamics* (New York: The Ronald Press, 1960), Chapters 8, 9, 10.

Assuming, however, that basically you are a fairly secure person who wants to be a good therapist, let us consider what positive actions you should take to help a child gain the self-confidence he in all likelihood badly needs. First of all, just speaking his name when he comes in (sweet music to any ear) will make him feel wanted. Early in your acquaintance with a pupil who is aware of his speech problem, ask him what he thinks about it and take time to listen to what he has to say. Seek a situation in which the pupil does something for you. Make him feel superior in some respect. Have him help you. Also create opportunities in which he can help others. Be interested in him as a person. Give him some freedom of choice in the selection of the therapeutic activities. If he performs a task because he has chosen to do it, he will do it better. The therapy should always be sufficiently difficult to make him work. It should provide, also, some opportunity for success. When it is necessary to do so, build up an acceptance of slow progress and possible failure as normal experiences in therapy and open the way for a new approach to the problem. Aspiration levels must be revised. Attitudes toward the self must be changed. Some youngsters must learn to live with less-than-good speech. Search for compensating factors. And then put adventure, excitement, and fun into your therapy. Help the child to tell you his troubles. Share the burdens and make the sharing pleasant. Help him to know himself and to like himself and to solve his problems.

36 Child centered play therapy may be explored by reading: Elise Hahn, "Indications for Direct, Nondirect and Indirect Methods in Speech Correction," *Journal of Speech and Hearing Disorders*, XXVI (August 1961), 230-36. Clark E. Moustakas, *Children in Play Therapy* (New York: McGraw-Hill Book Company, 1958), pp. 1-9, 59-100, 204-11. Virginia M. Axline, "Entering a Child's World Via Play Experiences," *Progressive Education*, XXVII (January 1950), 68-75.

Elaine Dorfiman, "Play Therapy" in Carl B. Rogers' *Client-Centered Therapy* (Boston: Houghton Mifflin Co., 1951), 235-77.
R. F. Hejna, *Speech Disorders and Non-Directive Therapy* (New York: McGraw-Hill Book Company, 1951), pp. 106-17.

Although the objectives and criteria heretofore considered apply to all speech therapy and you as a school therapist will spend a major portion of your time with articulation cases, nevertheless, stuttering and poor voice quality are serious problems. Let us review the prime considerations in planning therapy for these cases.

Stuttering

The annual statistical reports on the types of speech problems found in school populations show a marked reduction in the number of stutterers in schools which have had several years of speech therapy.* You will, nevertheless, have your stutterers and you will often be judged by your success with them. Some of these cases will be in the secondary stages and present problems that will challenge your ingenuity; more of them, however, will be in the primary stages and in all probability will respond to wisely designed therapy.

First of all, remember you are in a school and to a degree (sometimes a very significant one) you may manipulate a child's environment to produce situations from which he receives ego satisfaction and in which he may communicate with a minimum amount of stress. It takes work, but you are in a laboratory filled with endless materials. Your therapy room is a part of the environment in which the child spends the major portion of his waking hours. It is in school that the greatest demands are made on him for good speech, and it is also in school that he may most effectively influence the happenings of the day by the use of good speech. It is your responsibility to recognize and use these many resources.

Often a child in the early stages of stuttering is almost unconscious of any speech problem. During this period of his life he is learning many things and frequently something as simple as a reduction in demands made upon him and commands given him by his mother, and also his teacher, will relieve the speech difficulty.

* Annual Reports of Speech Correction Programs, State of Illinois, years 1950-1951 through 1962-1963.

This is the type of stutterer with whom you may work in groups of other like stutterers or articulation cases. As long as the atmosphere of the group is a free and pleasant one in which each child participates happily, the children may all grow in their mastery of speech.

The child, however, whose stuttering begins later and who struggles with speech may be served more wisely on an individual basis. The causes of his stuttering are probably deeper than a slightly bewildered frustration which results in a few blocks in speech.

Several approaches to the problem of stuttering, all used concurrently, may converge to make an effective therapy design. Situations must be created in which the stutterer can feel satisfied with himself. This might happen within the therapy room when he succeeds in some activity, or outside the room in a situation where giving a genuine service increases self-respect. For example, he might help the therapist prepare materials for young children by cutting out a wooden clown on the jigsaw at home. In this ego-building therapy the classroom teacher and the other staff members can be of help. If you will search, you will find a place in the stutterer's daily routine where he can do something for which he can be given honest recognition.

During the therapy session you will be working directly on reducing communicative stress. You will have him observe carefully what his tongue, lips, mouth, and face are doing. You will go through the spasms with him and then teach him to approach them more easily. You will emphasize his periods of normal speech. You will locate words, subjects, and situations which appear to trigger the stuttering, and then work to reduce the fears which color these spots. You will teach him to talk at all times in the easiest possible manner. When progress is noted you will seek opportunities within the school as well as outside in which he can reinforce his new speech.

From the beginning of the therapy you will want to have a close relationship with his parents and with his teachers. Your first objective will be to learn more about the boy through their knowledge of him and their reactions to him. Second, you will want them to know what you are attempting to do and to counsel them in attitudes and practices that are helpful in the day-by-day relationships with stutterers.

Often the most helpful service you can give parents is just listening to their frustrations. Let them talk until they have talked out their problems. Then you can begin to explain the child's speech problem as you see it and what you are doing to relieve it. How deeply you can probe into parent-child relationships will depend upon your professional training, your experience, and your native intuition. The latter is difficult to assay. You yourself will have to decide whether or not you are now ready, or perhaps ever will be ready, to counsel parents on matters concerning family relationships. It is often wiser to refer parents to professional counselors. Usually a young therapist in the first years of experience should restrict parental counseling to suggestions for the relief of obvious stress-creating situations and should extend only as much therapy into the home as it appears the family can tolerate.

Group counseling with parents of stutterers offers an opportunity for both parents to meet others with like problems and to talk about stuttering more objectively than is usually possible in a private session. It is always easier to bear a burden when you know someone else has a similar one; so there is therapeutic relief for parents in a group situation.

Through a close relationship with the classroom teacher and other school persons who know the child, you can gain information that will help you in planning the therapy. You can also enlist their assistance in utilizing situations which will give the child needed experiences. It may well be that some interpretation of the clinical point of view concerning stuttering will be necessary before teachers can give you their full cooperation. Do this in the spirit of one professional person talking to another and assuming that each, competent in his own work, respects the specialized knowledge and skills of the other.

Voice

In every school population you will find some children whose voices could be improved by therapy. It is suspected that these children are frequently overlooked in a speech survey. If you listen critically, one thing you will certainly hear is the voice which is excessively nasal. There may be functional reasons for this, but not always, so have a careful examination. Then there are the denasal voices due to growths or allergies. A medical referral is indicated, and after the needed care has been given, therapy may start. Harsh, strident voices show abuse and again a medical referral should be made. There are probably more vocal nodules in the schools than are being found. Occasionally unilateral paralysis of the vocal cords occurs in school children.

A juvenile, high-pitched male voice which is inappropriate to a boy's age and physical development, may be caused by psychological problems or, if not changed, may contribute to psychological problems. Cases of this type should be your serious concern.

> A rather striking example was a freshman boy who had a very high-pitched voice. He had all the physical characteristics of a well matured adolescent and the medical examination revealed no problem. In learning to know the family, the therapist found that the father had run away with another woman. The boy greatly resented this and hated the father.
>
> While working to get a sustained note, it was observed that when the boy coughed or cleared his throat he had a low baritone voice. Beginning with that, the therapist soon was able to have him produce a good voice; however, he was uncomfortable about using it.
>
> A plan was made to have him make the voice change during the Christmas holidays. In the meantime the school social worker conferred with the family and the boy's teachers. When he returned to school he used the new voice. There was a complete change in his personality. From a sullen, withdrawn boy, he became a socially very active one. He began to date girls and entered into several school activities. He no longer rejected his maleness.

Adolescent girls, too, often have voices which are characterized by a weak, husky quality. Advice on vocal hygiene and maturity will usually take care of these. You should check them, however, every six months until the voice improves and this may be for a period of even two years. Frequently the male nasal voice, too, is taken care of by maturity.

Your therapy will frequently involve a limited and relaxed easy use of the voice. Good posture is the first step. Here you work to retrain muscles. Show pictures of them and teach how to break old habits and establish new ones. Breathing? Yes, it is something to do and may help, but it is possible to get a good voice with little attention to breathing. Humming oh-oh-oh on a pitch that is comfortable, usually a middle C for girls, is a way to start. Too much emphasis need not be given range and variety. These are not needed in speech therapy. In fact, too wide a range might be dangerous.

During all voice therapy much emphasis should be put on listening and recording. The pupils should be taught to label and analyze the voice sounds heard. The first step is to have the student recognize the problem and want to do something about it. This may present a real challenge in some voice cases. The example on page 86 shows what one therapist did to interest three high-school girls.

Other Problems

After all articulation, stuttering, and voice problems have been diagnosed, you will still have a few more cases. These will be the children who have cleft palates, are cerebral palsied, are delayed in developing speech, or have other special problems. In working with them you will often be following the prescriptions of university or hospital clinics. It is also quite possible that many of these children

37   Compare the Oregon and the Wisconsin plans for the speech rehabilitation of a person with a cleft palate.
      Herold Lillywhite, "Teamwork in the Oregon Cleft Palate Program," *Journal of Speech and Hearing Disorders*, XXI (March 1956), 18-24.
      Wayne B. Slaughter and Gretchen M. Phair, "Research and Service Combined for Complete Cleft Palate Care," *Journal of Speech and Hearing Disorders*, XVII (June 1952), 123-28.

will have voice, articulation, or rhythm problems and that group work with other such children will be helpful. Some individual therapy, however, is usually needed. Parent and teacher conferences will be frequent and the speech therapy plan may be one which encompasses all of the child's activities. It is not the purpose of this book to outline the special routines required for these children.

We now turn to the therapy session, the heart of the whole matter. The screening, the diagnosis, and the scheduling have been done, the room is prepared and the materials are selected. You are at last ready to plan that all-important first session.

First Day

On that first day, be sure to teach something. When the youngster goes home he will be asked, "What did you learn in the new speech class?" He should have an answer. Possibly it may be how to say your name. It may be how to find the speech room. It may be to recite a rhyme clearly. It may be that he learned something about voice and that some sounds use it and some do not. Whatever it is, fix the fact of achievement firmly in the pupil's mind before he leaves. You might prepare a young child to answer his parents' questions like this:

> Her name is Miss Allen and we go to the end of the hall and turn toward the stairway. There is a picture of a little boy on the door. I like speech class.

While a child's need is the first consideration, such controlling factors as available time, space, materials, resources, and your own competence must be recognized. Determine the immediate objective, scrutinize your facilities, and manipulate the latter to serve the former. That is the essence of therapy planning.

38   What basic items do you need?
       D. Bell and E. L. Pross, "A Medicine Bag for the Speech Correctionist," *Journal of Speech and Hearing Disorders,* XVII (December 1952), 397-400.

Continued Planning

A well organized plan includes these considerations: First, the materials to be used are readily available. The tape recorder is set up, the word list is on the chalkboard, or the drill cards are sorted for use. As time progresses the preceding sessions should be reviewed to determine whether or not their objectives have been mastered. This review also gives each pupil a chance to demonstrate something he can do. Often you may have to reteach. Next in order is the introduction of new tasks and activities. During this time you will usually make the assignment. Finally, what has been mastered is summarized.

It is important that the child develop a feeling of confidence in what he does; therefore, begin with a task in which success is very probable. The actual correction of errors can wait for a time. For example:

In the first therapy session for articulatory problems, you might have the youngsters distinguish between grossly unlike sounds, *th* and *k*, *b* and *s*. When you have their attention fixed on listening to your models and when confidence has been built by experiencing success, move on to somewhat similar sounds, *f*, *s*, or *s*, *sh*. Continue your therapy using the auditory, visual, and possibly the tactile approaches. "Close your eyes and I will make the *b* sound, but if I change to the *k* sound, open your eyes." "Watch my lips when I say *b*. What happens? Now watch when I say *k-k-k*. Any difference?" "Let's watch our own lips in the mirror: *b-b-b—k-k-k*. What happens to our lips when we say *b*? When we say *k*? Where in our mouths do we feel *b-b-b*? Where do we feel *k*?"

It is important that a child be able to distinguish between correct

Figure 12. Let's watch our tongues.

and incorrect speech in his own production. Some pupils do not know that they have a speech problem. Many are vaguely aware of something wrong with their speech but cannot identify the exact errors. The child must first become aware of the speech of others and then be able to contrast the correct or "good" sound with the incorrect or "bad" sound. Next he must learn to recognize his own error or "bad" sound. In all likelihood he hears his own speech as he thinks it rather than as he produces it. Getting him to listen and evaluate may take time but it is the most important part of the therapy. The correct mental concept of the sound must police the ear and the mouth before the desired production can become habitual.

39 How does this author support the use of auditory stimulation as a basic training technique?
Margaret E. Hall, "Auditory Factors In Functional Articulatory Speech Defects," *Journal of Experimental Education*, VII (December 1938), 110-32.

Some children may be helped to identify sounds more readily by your touching the lips or the throat. Several therapy periods will undoubtedly be needed to establish recognition and production of a new sound. Motivational materials which can be adapted to each child's rate of progress may be used, but care should be exercised to secure continuous participation of every member of the group.

After a new sound has been mastered, its use in various positions may be taught through nonsense syllables. Then you move on to words, phrases, sentences, and finally conversation. These activities,

40 You may find a teacher of reading or a manual for teaching phonics to primary children disagreeing somewhat with what you have been taught about sounds. In the article, "To Isolate or Not to Isolate in Speech Therapy," *Exceptional Children*, XXV (February 1959), 247, Dr. Clara Mawhinney interprets very clearly the therapist's viewpoint concerning phonetics.

of course, will cover many weeks. The methods used should vary frequently. All sessions for pupils with articulation or voice problems should include auditory training. Very few of these people will come to you with sufficiently acute auditory sensitivity or with a developed ability to distinguish sounds. If they had these they would not need you.

41   In the following references you will find discussions of listening skills as they apply to reading. Many of these also apply to speech. List the ones which do.

Marion Monroe, *Growing Into Reading* (Chicago: Scott, Foresman & Company, 1951), pp. 110-40.

D. H. Russell and E. F. Russell, *Listening Aids Through the Grades* (New York: Bureau of Publications, Teachers College, Columbia University, 1959).

The child should listen to you, to his classmates, to himself, and to recordings. At times you may want to use sound amplifiers, such as a cardboard tube, a milk carton, an auditory training unit, your tape recorder, a wooden shoe, or a hearing aid. The mirror, the chalkboard, stories, pictures, and games all contribute to therapy.

The physical comfort of the pupils should be considered. Young children should not be kept in one position too long. Little feet get restless. Activities should be planned which involve some body movement. Children may step to the chalkboard and point out a picture or word. They may play a game which involves moving along in a line or one in which seats are exchanged. Personality differences should be recognized. The shy child may be taught to "stand tall" and "talk big." The aggressive child may be given command or service responsibilities. The child beaten down by failure may be put in situations where he cannot help but win.

Making the assignment affords one of the most important opportunities for sound therapy. First of all, don't wait until the last minute to do it. At an opportune time make an exact, concrete assignment. Example: "We have been learning to say *f-f-f*. For Tuesday, let's all have lists in our notebooks of five words beginning with *f* and another five ending with *f*. Here are some." On the board write *fight, fling, Philip,* and *loaf, muff, cough.* "What is different about the last ones? Yes, sometimes we find the sound *f* written *ph* or *gh*. How can you locate other words? Yes, by careful listening. Other ways? Yes, in your readers and in the picture dictionary." If the child has learned to produce the new sound, he can practice certain words until he is certain he knows them. A good assignment time might be after he brushes his teeth at night. You will find yourself saying such things as these to your children: "How will the bathroom mirror be a help to you in the *f* sound? Let's all look at our hand mirrors and watch our lower lips as we say *f-f-f*. On the top of the new page in your notebook write *F*. Make two lists. I'll give you two starts:"

1.	four	1.	puff
2.		2.	
3.		3.	
4.		4.	
5.		5.	

At the next meeting always check on the outside assignment. The therapy sessions are several days apart, so you have to develop continuity. An assignment well taught on Monday and carefully reviewed on Wednesday establishes a bridge which joins the first therapy session with the second. Such bridges are needed. Be sure that you do not ask too much of the child and provide helpful reminders he can carry away with him.

> 42   How may the criteria used by the following authors in evaluating reading and art workbooks be used also to judge speech workbooks and speech activity materials?
> D. H. Russell, *Children Learn to Read* (New York: Ginn & Company, 1949), pp. 99-118.
> Charles D. Gaitskell, *Children and Their Art* (New York: Harcourt, Brace & World, Inc., 1958), pp. 353-55.

In summary, a complete plan for therapy states both your objectives and those of the student. Certain criteria are met. The materials and activities to be used are selected beforehand. The past work is reviewed, the assignment checked, and if need be, time must be taken for reteaching. New work is presented in various ways with major emphasis usually on auditory stimulation or correct sound production. An assignment is planned. Reinforcement of gains is accomplished through interesting activities and games. And finally, the accomplishment of the period is summarized in a positive manner.

> Today we have learned to make the final *r*. We also learned what happens to this sound in some parts of our country. Keep your ears open for radio or television speech. Who will be the first to spot an *r* used differently than we do?

Of course you will not have enough time to write detailed plans for every lesson. You can make a master plan to cover four to six lessons and then each day keep a brief running record. You may wish to use a lesson plan book or you may wish to keep a record sheet for each child. After each date you should indicate what was accomplished and what was assigned, and perhaps what difficulties were encountered. Learn to teach with a pencil in hand and to make your notes during and between classes.

To be a successful therapist you must be a bit of an actor. You play to your audience. Open every lesson with some interest-creating device: a joke, a story, an exciting question, a picture, a gadget, something that will make the youngster wonder what is coming next. Have every pupil leave your class with a clear knowledge of what has been accomplished, or occasionally not accomplished. Nebulous efforts at personality-building through pleasant little conversations usually accomplish very little. You have only a small portion of time to make your impact felt. If you will keep in mind two facts, first that better speech may do more for a child's personality growth than any other single accomplishment, and second, that you are the person whose prime responsibility is to get better speech, you will recognize your basic function, namely, providing speech therapy. Yes, exploring and removing causes contributing to poor speech are very important aspects of your work, but concurrently with these activities you must help the child to change his speech from what it is to something much better.

Conclusions

When used by an alert therapist the preceding suggestions will enrich programs for the rehabilitation of speech. We have indicated the supplementary resources available both in and out of the schools, and have reviewed some of the principles which may serve as guides in planning speech therapy. No attempt has been made to give detailed suggestions for procedures. Each of you will want to develop your own plans for alleviating speech problems. To be effective, therapy must reflect your individual philosophy and beliefs. It must be your own. We have attempted to emphasize the unique opportunities offered speech therapists who practice in educationally oriented environments and who have access to the resources found in many American communities. ᘓᘓᘓ

IN THE PRECEDING SECTIONS WE HAVE CONSIDERED MANY OF THE FACTORS which contribute to a speech therapy program. We have discussed the room, the survey and scheduling procedures, the school and community resources, and plans for therapy. This section will consider some of the more personal problems, such as considerations in locating the first position and relationships with colleagues and the public. Finally, taking a brief look at what appear to be the trends in American life for the next two decades, we will try to envision the part our profession will play in the future.

3 *the future*

Legal Requirements

Schools are regulated by state laws and all teachers must obtain state certification. The legal requirements in the various states are far from uniform. You, therefore, must plan your college program to meet the qualifying standards of the state in which you wish to practice therapy. Information concerning these standards may be obtained from the Office of the Superintendent of Public Instruction, which is located in the capital city of the state. Get this information yourself and know that you can be legally qualified. There is a difference between the preparation needed for clinical work or work with adults and the preparation needed for work in a school setting. Many states recognize this difference.

43   What is the philosophy underlying the approval and accreditation of schools? How does this affect speech correction?
Hugo Gregory, "State Approval and Accreditation of Public Schools," ASHA, III (May 1961), 145-47.

Locating a Job

Let us begin thinking about securing a position. You are going into the working world during a fortunate era when there will be many jobs available, but you will want to secure the one for which you are best suited. Where is it? Your first point of inquiry should be the teacher placement office in your college. Visit it to make sure that your papers and references are all in order. If you want someone to write a recommendation for you, you should obtain his permission to use his name. Be sure to include your major professors among your references. Some employers also like to have statements from persons who know you in ways other than professional. A family doctor, a clergyman, a banker, or a lawyer are people who could be asked for character references. The placement office will have vacancies listed and through it you may have opportunities to interview superintendents who are seeking therapists.

Notices of open positions are obtainable also through the American Speech and Hearing Association (*Trends*), the National Society for Crippled Children and Adults, some state teachers' organizations, and commercial agencies. If you are interested in a particular locality, you may write letters of inquiry to state or county offices of education, or directly to local superintendents of schools. You, of course, never apply for a position you know is filled, but you may ask if there will be any vacancies. The letter of inquiry should be brief, courteous, and free from error. Have it checked and rechecked before you mail it.

The Interview

When you get a nibble, follow it if possible with a personal interview. Many schools will pay the expenses of a visit. This not only gives the superintendent an opportunity to see you, but it also enables you to see him and his system. You can expect some general questions about your training and your therapy experience, but he will be interested, too, in your general philosophy of education and especially about your interests in speech correction. He may ask how you would set up a program, how you would select students, and what you envision as your place in the total school program. Or he may only ask you how much salary you require. You, in turn, will

want to know several things about the position and what will be
expected of you. Learn who is directly responsible for the supervision of the speech program. Discover where you would belong on
the organizational chart. Is speech correction a part of a larger program for exceptional children? Is there state aid and supervision?
Ask about the attitude of the principals and the teachers toward
the speech correction program. How satisfactory a therapist was
your predecessor? Ask what schools you are to serve and their approximate enrollments. You might ask to visit one of the speech
rooms to learn what equipment is available and what may need to
be requisitioned. If a new program is to be initiated, you will want
to know answers to such questions as these: What has stimulated the
present interest in establishing a program? What has been done to
acquaint the community and the school personnel with the plan?
You may have to do an extensive job of interpretation.

The School System

This is the time to get a general picture of the school system. Note
particularly the health, the guidance, and the psychological and
social services. Ask a few questions about community facilities for
child welfare. What teacher welfare services are available, such as
health insurance, teachers' pensions, and credit unions? You will
want to know about local living conditions and their cost.

You must not expect to find a situation in which every problem has been met and solved. Such would be, indeed, a dull job.
Nevertheless, you should go into any position with your eyes open.
Remember that the more difficult the problems are, the greater are
the opportunities for your growth. Have recent bond issues or increases in school taxes been defeated? There are happy schools and
unhappy ones. How long do teachers stay? What are their educational backgrounds? How many are home-town people? If the
teacher turnover is rapid, if the educational level is low, or if there
is a predominance of local people, it may not be a very desirable
location. When it is possible to do so, contact the former speech
therapist and ask about her experiences, but reserve judgment until
you know all the facts.

Weigh carefully the pros and cons of this particular job against what you can offer and decide whether or not you should consider accepting it. Then, and only then, ask about the pay. The initial salary may not be so important as is the opportunity to be on a regular schedule that offers attractive increases. Study the salary schedule carefully and have a clear understanding of where you would start and where you could expect to be within five years. Are there requirements and rewards for advanced training? Would it be a wise thing to remain in this system several years? Are there any attractive unattached members of the opposite sex around? Finally, take a good long walk around the town and decide whether or not you would want to live there.

After one position has been accepted you should notify all other schools or agencies with whom you have had contacts that you are no longer seeking employment and also thank them for the courtesies given you.

44   Why are repeated appraisals necessary for a professional person's growth?
     Herold Lillywhite, "Toward a Philosophy of Professional Behavior," *ASHA*, III, No. 2 (February 1961), 39-42.

You and the Public

Speech correction, being somewhat different from the traditional activities conducted in a school, needs frequent interpretation to the public. If not called upon to do so, you should unobtrusively seek opportunities to talk before groups of all types—P.T.A., Mothers' Clubs, noon luncheon groups, service clubs, church groups, and many of the civic and social organizations. Explain the objectives of speech therapy, describe which types of speech are considered defective, and how you work. Emphasize the fact that you anticipate no miraculous cures, but you do expect improved speech in most of the cases, and keep your remarks nontechnical and brief.

Parents in Groups

Parent-Teacher Association meetings offer opportunities to meet the parents in a fairly informal situation. Invitations may be issued to visit the speech room and indirectly the parents may learn to know the program and the teacher. These are times to show the room and the equipment. Parents, fathers in particular, like to see how the gadgets work. You might test a few ears and record some speech. One caution though—general meetings are poor places for discussions with parents. If a problem is worthy of their time and yours, it deserves an uninterrupted conference in a quiet place. Make an appointment for the parent to come during your office time. On P.T.A. night there are too many curious eyes and ears lurking about your door. Serious discussions with parents should always be private ones.

Another type of group meeting you may want to have is a partially social one. Mothers, particularly those of very young children, enjoy getting together. Some therapists have found that teas or coffee sessions for mothers of kindergarteners, at which talks on early speech development are given, have been very well received. These affairs might be held as early as the spring before the children start to school.

Parent Conferences

For successful therapy the cooperation of the child's parents is necessary. They must understand what is being done and why, and give whatever assistance they can. How are good relationships between the parents and the therapist established?

45 What are apt to be the feelings of parents who have a child who is handicapped?
Eugene McDonald, *Understand Those Feelings* (Pittsburgh: Stanwix House, Inc., 1962), pp. 1-32.

First, there is the conference. This should be early in the year, but with a caseload of 70 or 100, you'll not be able to see every mother in September. However, if you arrange appointments on your office afternoon and schedule them carefully so each has from fifteen to twenty minutes, you'll be able to see the most urgent ones before Thanksgiving. Telephone calls are a second best means of communicating, and finally notes.

When a parent has a conference with you regarding his child, you must be aware always that the parent is bringing to that meeting his concern about the most precious thing in his life. Try to see the problems from his point of view and give him plenty of opportunity to talk out his feelings. An authoritative attitude on your part will not win a friend, nor will you make a convert. Home calls will be beneficial primarily to you and your understanding of the child, but when you want to discuss a very serious situation or to make a suggestion that may be difficult for a parent to accept, do it at school where the professional atmosphere will give you more stature.

Keep the conversation on the subject of the conference. After a few friendly opening remarks, get down to business. You may want to take notes. If you do, ask the mother if she minds, explaining that you want to keep fresh in your mind what she tells you. Watch your choice of words carefully. Never say, "Your boy's speech is substandard for his age." Rather say, "It seems to us that Hector is not making the speech progress he should for a boy his age and we wonder if there isn't something we can do to help him." Don't attempt to tell all you know about speech in the first interview. Save some for a second and maybe a third, and above all, listen to the mother. She knows the boy better than you do. Send her away with a constructive suggestion, such as a little plan for having Hector recite nursery rhymes to the baby sister, offer the blessing at the dinner table, or teach the dog to follow certain commands, such as *run, come,* and *roll over.* Then ask her to let you know after two weeks what progress the boy has made.

Always endeavor to have professional discussions at school. Discourage telephone calls to you at home. Tell the caller politely that you do not have your records and give him a time when he may call you at school. Landladies or apartment mates should not overhear your conversation and you should not carry your work into your free time.

Some home visits are necessary. The mother may have small children and be unable to come to school, or you may think that you are missing something in your understanding of the child by not seeing the home situation. Whatever the reason, it is polite to make an appointment. Don't embarrass the mother by catching her unawares. The home call should be brief and of a semisocial nature. You're there to get the atmosphere of the home rather than a detailed case history. If your visits take you into some rather unpleasant spots,

don't be too shocked. This child shall rise. On the other hand, if
your call takes you into the finest house in the town, don't be awed.
There may be problems there too.

> 46   What thought have you given the father and his part in the problem?
>   Eugene T. McDonald, *Understanding Those Feelings* (Pittsburgh: Stanwix
>   House, Inc., 1962), pp. 118-36.

There will be times when you'll want to invite the parents to
watch some therapy. Here is what one school therapist did:

> Miss Hines, the first-grade teacher, had several children with severe
> articulation problems; so she and Miss Benson, the speech therapist,
> planned a demonstration for all the mothers. Invitations were sent
> asking them to come to a "Good Speech Tea." When the mothers ar-
> rived they were taken to the first-grade room where Miss Hines taught a
> speech lesson. First, she had the children do speech calisthenics. "Stand,
> arms out on *ee,* touch shoulders on *oh-ee-oh-ee-oh.* Arms straight up on
> *l-l-l.* Touch shoulders on *b-l—l-b.* Swing arms around and around on
> *whooo.*" This was repeated. Then they made their motors hum—*mmm.*
> They were seated. Now they had to be very, very quiet because this took
> very sharp ears. When you heard the quiet sound you closed your eyes,
> but when you heard a loud one you opened your eyes—*sss, ggg—sss—ggg—
> sss.*
>
> Miss Hines then showed them a picture of Peter, Peter Pumpkin Eater
> and they all said the rhyme together. This was followed by more pictures
> and rhymes. The lesson closed with each one giving his name in a clear
> first-grade voice.
>
> The mothers were then invited into the lounge where Miss Benson
> talked about speech correction and the additional work she was giving
> some children. She passed out a leaflet on "How I Can Help My Child
> to Talk." It gave some simple directions for forming good speech habits.
> A discussion followed. She told them that the children she took for speech
> help would occasionally bring home activities sheets which would give
> suggestions for help from the mothers. She asked that they sign the papers
> and return them, which would indicate that the work had been done.
> Tea was served.

While some parents can give speech help pleasantly and unobtrusively, others develop a pattern of constant nagging or an emotionally charged reward technique.

> Mrs. Crone, president of the P.T.A. and leader in her church group, had
> a daughter, Ann, whose lisp was very noisy. Nothing cute about this one.
> The mother decided she would correct the child every time the error

occurred and also that each clear sound would be rewarded with, "Ann is a good girl now and mother loves her." After a few months of this treatment the poor child began to retreat into silence and it was only with difficulty that anyone could get her to talk. The therapist had to speak very plainly to the mother before she would stop tormenting the girl. Here was a case of any speech being better than no speech. It took months of understanding therapy before Ann began to respond with better speech.

You will be wise to know the parents quite well before you suggest much therapy at home.

47   What points do these articles emphasize regarding counseling with parents of children who have speech handicaps?
E. K. Sanders, "Counseling Parents of Stuttering Children," *Journal of Speech and Hearing Disorders*, XXIV (August 1959), 262-71.
Edward E. Matis, "Psychotherapeutic Tools for Parents," *Journal of Speech and Hearing Disorders*, XXVI (May 1961), 164-70.

Troublesome Problems

One of the advantages of being a speech therapist is that you are free from some of the woes that plague most teachers. For example, you do not have children in large groups, you have few discipline problems, you do not have to collect the milk money, and you do not have the frustrations that accompany giving grades. But you do not escape entirely. There will be problems. Let us consider these cases.

The Smart-Aleck

Alfred was a twelve-year-old boy whose lisp had defied correction. The records indicated that little in speech therapy had been practiced. The preceding therapist had spent most of the time keeping him and his friend, Bill, quiet. The first thing Miss Morrow did was schedule the two boys for different periods. She put Alfred with two fourteen-year-old boys who stuttered and who appeared to be very cooperative youngsters. She then planned activities which began the minute the boys entered the room and lasted all period. While the two boys recorded a conversation, she worked with Alfred on sound discrimination. Later while she worked with the other boys, Alfred made a list of good *s* words from a prepared tape. Miss Morrow returned to him for the last few minutes and together they checked his written record.

Each therapy period was filled with planned activities. In the meantime Miss Morrow made an extensive study of Alfred's history. She interviewed his present and previous teachers, the principal, the physical education instructor, the music teacher, and the nurse. She was looking primarily for two things. First, was there any physical or emotional reason for his behavior? Second, what kind of a boy was he and what were his interests?

The interview with the mother was postponed until a later date. There were two reasons for this. Alfred hated to have anyone talk to his mother and Miss Morrow wanted to know the boy before she offered any suggestions. There appeared to be no physical problem and except for what one teacher described as "inborn devilishness" no psychological problems. Miss Morrow did discover that his one consuming interest was horses and Western movies.

Using these interests as guides, she developed unit therapy projects. After Alfred had prepared a short talk on types of horses, he gave it for his class. Later he helped Miss Morrow make a Western movie paper roll for the first graders. Somewhere along the way the behavior problem disappeared and by spring the *s* was a sharp one.

The Uncooperative Teacher

Miss Higgins had taught in the same room for twenty-five years. Her fourth-graders knew their arithmetic and could spell down the other fourth grades in the school. Her room ran on an exact schedule and woe to anyone who interrupted it. Unfortunately she had three youngsters with serious speech problems. They were transfers from a school where there had been no speech services and Miss Gale, the therapist, knew that they were in real need of help. After several conferences, Miss Higgins grudgingly agreed to a certain schedule. During the first four weeks the children failed four times to come to speech class. Miss Higgins felt that what was happening in the classroom just could not be missed. Miss Gale offered to arrange for different periods. This was done but in a few weeks that time, too, could not be spared from the classroom. In a third conference Miss Higgins mentioned her concern about the children's spelling. Their performance was ruining the record of the class. That gave Miss Gale an idea and she suggested that possibly intensive speech work would improve the children's ability to recognize sounds and thereby improve their spelling. Miss Higgins pounced on the idea. She was desperate. Her claim to fame was at stake. The time allotted for therapy was increased and the children never missed a session. Miss Gale worked on sound recognition, sound discrimination, and sound production. The spelling book was the source book. It brought results. Not only was the speech of all three youngsters greatly improved, but two became excellent spellers and the third could pass the tests. Miss Higgins was a convert to speech therapy. Never again did she question its value.

Yourself

Youngsters of all ages like to have an attractive teacher. They notice everything you wear. Not only should you always present that well-scrubbed look, but also your clothing should be attractive and well styled. The professional man does not arrive at school in casual attire. The girl therapist wears clothing that is attractive and varied from day to day. Youngsters, particularly in junior high school and up, are very critical observers. And all of us must remember that in speech therapy we work very close to our pupils.

Good living quarters are vitally important. The school office usually has listings of available rooms and apartments. You might be wise to take a room temporarily and look around a bit before you decide to go into an apartment which might require a lease. Also, before you join forces with some new acquaintance, wait a bit until you are sure you won't be miserable together.

Your Leisure

A young person going into a new town has to find a place for himself in the social life. How to meet people you would enjoy knowing may appear to be a problem. Here are some suggestions: Attend your church, introduce yourself to the pastor, and join the organizations for people your age. Inquire about clubs or hobby groups. Usually the "Y's" have social programs. A few warnings: Don't confine your activities to groups composed exclusively of your own sex. The others are more fun. Don't join the high-school age group even though you are not much older. You are now an adult; high-school students are not. Neither should you know only teachers. Fine as they are, you see enough of them in school. You should spend part of your free time getting to know people with other interests.

Since you are a teacher, your conduct will be expected to conform with the best in the community and sometimes to be better than the best. Is this fair? Yes—of your own free choice you became a teacher. When you made that decision you consciously or unconsciously entered into a pact with the ideals of the American public. That pact is to be at all times and under all circumstances a person whom

children respect. Ours is not a profession for weaklings. The image
of a speech therapist is that of a first-class person. Keep it so.

48   Many useful materials may be secured from sources listed in:
      Suttles, P. H., ed., *Elementary Teachers Guide to Free Curriculum Mate-*
      rials (Randolph, Wis.: Educators Progress Service, 1960).

You'll have a good time. There is a good bit of evidence to show
that speech therapists are popular and outstanding leaders in any
group. In fact, two of the difficulties found in catching up with the
demand for therapists have been, first, superintendents have liked
them so well that they urged the therapists to take attractive administrative positions, and second, the little fellow with the bow
and arrow aims straight at the therapists. They get married. Many
of the victims in the latter group, however, return to teach another
day. In them lies the hope for a stable profession.

THE LONG LOOK FORWARD

What does the future hold for you who are going to work as a
speech therapist in the schools? You have now reached an age where
you may exercise a degree of control over choices you will make.
To do this intelligently you should acquaint yourself with a few
facts of life in America.

Looking ahead into the next few decades, you might ask these
questions: Where will be the great centers of population? Where
will the population remain static? Who will be the immigrants and
the migrants? What will be the education of the people? How will
they be employed? Will there be changes in the proportions of
people in the various age brackets? And finally, how will all this
affect the speech correction profession? There is no better way to
become informed than by reading the reports of the Bureau of Census; so let us consider some of them.

These studies of population trends are not merely abstract numbers, but are the behavior patterns of human beings as they grow
up, seek an education, enter the labor market, move about, establish
families of their own, and contribute to all the activities which make
up the total of American life. These numbers represent experiences
you will be encountering all through your lives.

The census report of 1960 gave the total population in our country as 180,000,000. Placing the birth rate at its present level, adding some improvement in mortality, and keeping the net immigration figure about where it is, it is estimated that by 1970 the population will be 214,000,000 and by 1980 it will increase to 260,000,000. If the present rate is continued, during your working years, which will be about forty, the population should double. Predictions of this sort are indeed a hazardous venture. Except for war or other major catastrophies, the chief variable is the birth rate. An economic depression would affect that. While few can predict with confidence future population growth, no such limitation restricts our predicting the number of people now alive who will reach certain significant ages in the future.

Here are some important comparisons of population growth (*152*). Between 1955 and 1960 the average annual number of persons becoming 14 years of age was 1,700,000. Between 1960 and 1965 it will be 3,200,000. Between 1965 and 1970 it will grow to 3,900,000, and between 1970 and 1975 it will be above 4,000,000 yearly. Another study * estimates that in 1980 the persons between the ages of 5 and 17 will number 67,550,000.

How will these increases in the school-age population affect the demand for speech therapists? Will an increase in the number of therapists alone meet the expanding needs? Will new techniques for serving larger groups have to be developed?

Population change from a social and economic point of view has three major dimensions: the changes in sheer size, which we have noted very briefly, changes in composition, and changes in geographic distribution. We will now consider the latter two.

Who are the workers? One significant study (*178*) shows that 23,600,000 workers will be in goods-producing industries, and 33,100,000 will be in service-producing industries. There will be more white-collar workers than blue-collar workers and there is nothing in the offing that will change this contour of the work force. Indeed, automation will increase the ratio.

One population group which demands careful study is the

* *Status and Trends: Vital Statistics, Education and Public Finance* (Washington, D.C.: Research Division, National Education Association, 1959), Table 3, p. 6.

Negroes. In 1960 they constituted about 10.5 per cent of all Americans. For many years they have been moving out of the South to the North and the West. The net movement from thirteen Southern states in the past decade was 1.5 million. This was very largely a movement from rural to urban areas. Most of the migrants were young adults. In the Northern states, over nine-tenths of all Negroes live in the metropolitan areas, primarily in the central cities. States which presently have more than a million Negroes are New York, Texas, Georgia, North Carolina, Louisiana, and Illinois. These people are striving to improve their way of life by securing the opportunities to work and live on an equal basis with other Americans.

The years of schooling completed by the adult population 25 years of age and over, computed for three twenty-year periods, indicate significant changes.*

In 1940, 13.7 per cent of the population had less than five years of schooling. By 1980 it is estimated that this percentage will be reduced to 4.1. During the same period the percentage of people having sixteen or more years of education will increase from 4.6 to 10.4.

The change from blue-collar to white-collar employment, the rising cultural status of the Negro, and the increase in years of education for everyone, all will have an impact on our profession. Better jobs demand better speech. People will have the money to pay for more services in the schools and will also have the leisure to work on self-improvement. There may well be a great demand for therapy with adults. Note the great increase in the number of people going to college. How many of those will become speech therapists? Recruitment of the most competent young students for our profession will be one of your major responsibilities.

WHERE WILL THE PEOPLE BE LIVING?

In our dynamic economy we are free to move and we do. One American in five moves from one house to another every year (152). One in four lives in a state other than the one in which he was born.

* *Status and Trends: Vital Statistics, Education and Public Finance* (Washington, D.C.: Research Division, National Education Association, 1959), Table 5, p. 7.

People are moving to the West and the Southwest. Also, the coastal and shore-line states, along the Pacific, the Atlantic, the Gulf of Mexico, and the Great Lakes, are gaining in population. In 1960 two-thirds of the population lived in cities of 50,000 or over and in the nearby suburban countryside closely related to the city. Big central cities, however, declined in population. They grew only by annexation. On the other hand, small towns and rural areas constantly lost in population. In 1910, 31 per cent of all workers were on farms; in 1959, 9 per cent, and in 1970, only 6 per cent will work on the soil (152). These trends clearly indicate that a major portion of the positions in speech therapy will be found in and about the larger cities.

> 49   What social, economic, and political beliefs have always operated to affect the course of speech as part of all education? Choose one of the references cited in:
> Edgar W. Knight, *Education in the U.S.* (New York: Ginn and Company, 1951), p. 188.

In this bird's-eye glance of population changes, certain facts stand out very clearly. You are not going to be at a loss for pupils. Children are arriving in ever-increasing numbers. Whatever the percentage of speech problems found among them may be, and however successful the efforts to recruit therapists may be, the demand for your services will far exceed the number of available workers. This is going to mean that more efficient procedures must be developed. No longer can a therapist spend time running up and down corridors looking for children, or passively listening to one child name objects while three children remain idle. You must have the knowledge of speech, psychology, and education that will enable you to direct the utilization of new scientific media to the end that more children may have better therapy. You are going to have to plan programs that are flexible in meeting the ever-changing demands of a school population and individualized to the extent that each child's needs may be recognized and served. These growing concepts of what constitutes a good speech therapy program will result in demands for better and better educated personnel. For you, study will go on and on.

The current image of the speech therapist held by our professional colleagues and the lay public is going to have to change. No longer must we be regarded as charming young persons who sometimes do rather remarkable things for children's speech. Rather, we must be regarded as creative thinkers who produce results. Our job requires both research and therapy, and neither activity excludes the other.

Your public is also going to consist of growing numbers of more highly educated people, many of whom will be living in or near large metropolitan areas, so most of you will be working in large school systems. A majority of the workers will be in the service-giving occupations. These people will have a real need for good speech. Each year more older women will be employed. In this group there will undoubtedly be mature speech therapists. In certain areas there will be numbers of new migrants. As a result, there will be the need to correct regional speech or dialect. In some instances there will be a need for establishing English when another language is the mother tongue. You will find this fully discussed in Chreist's text, *Foreign Accent,* in this series. The continued decline in rural and small town populations will mean, of course, that only a few of you will find employment in these areas. From the standpoint of age, the great increases will be among the very young and the older groups. This indicates a growing need for preventative therapy and also for closer work with clinics which have geriatric practices. Thus emerges the future picture of our profession.

We have indicated some of the trends. Now let us be more specific. When your generation comes to the time of its greatest productivity, which is between 35 and 45 years of age, it will form the smallest segment of the total population. And when you consider that you will be among the small number of well educated people in your group, you will recognize not only your responsibility but also the almost limitless opportunity you will have to influence the tide of affairs. When in American history has any age group had a better chance?

Large Communities

It is apparent that most of you will be employed in city and suburban areas. That is where the great number of children will live. You may love the country, but there are many advantages to be found in these urban and suburban positions. You will probably be working in a program already established and under the direction of a consultant or a supervisor. You will need to be well-trained and you will need to keep learning your profession. There will be other therapists readily available for consultation and advice. The school will be staffed with nurses, doctors, audiologists, psychologists, and social workers. Your work will be more and more clinical in nature. Metropolitan areas usually have many medical, psychological, and social resources which may contribute to the solution of some speech problems. Universities which offer opportunities for advanced study and cooperative research are nearby. You will need to avail yourself of all these opportunities for growth. Professional meetings and conventions are held in large cities. Cultural advantages of many kinds are readily obtainable, and salary schedules will be better than those to which many of us have been accustomed.

There are, however, some knotty problems to be met. One, and it is found everywhere, is the matter of finances. Few, if any, states have modernized their tax laws sufficiently to provide adequate support for education. Another serious problem found particularly in the urban centers will be that of shifting populations. In any school there may be children from very different backgrounds and races. Thus, any kind of a grouping for therapy is difficult. In addition, many families move so frequently that you will barely get a therapy program started when many children will disappear into the great maw of statistics. Moreover, the sheer weight of numbers in the great cities necessitates certain rather exact regulations which will constrain and restrict your professional freedom. Changes will not be made quickly and at times this may prove irksome. The speech therapy program will be only a small segment of a gigantic operation and, as such, may sometimes appear to be overlooked or forgotten. This may become a source of frustration. There is great need for increased supervision in systems employing large numbers of therapists. Parent conferences frequently are difficult to arrange. City mothers are apt to be working mothers. Home calls may be impractical and often are discouraged. This lack of free communication makes therapy difficult. And, sad to report, the higher salary will be offset by the higher rent.

Small Communities

Perhaps you like to fish, hunt, and roam in the wide open spaces; so let us consider opportunities in the small towns and rural areas. While fewer therapists will be needed to serve this smaller population, yet nationwide, this is still largely an unserved group; so during your lifetime there will always be a demand for therapists in the less densely populated areas. Most of these jobs will be beginning programs, or not too long established ones. You, consequently, will have the exciting opportunity of putting your own ideas to work. You may make the program just about what you want it to be. You can pioneer. You will find in these communities a stable population and in a few years you will know all the families and the skeletons in each closet. You will be able to know all the teachers and children and have contacts with everyone from the superintendent on down. Community contacts, also, will be made directly. You'll meet and be able to talk to the specialists; you won't have to rely on the impersonality of second- or third-hand reports.

All education in rural regions is undergoing drastic reorganization. Many small districts are consolidating into one big one. You may have to inaugurate a speech program that covers a wide territory and serves many children, but you may have a model speech center in a consolidated school. Originality and creative thinking on your part will be demanded. You may be able to develop new approaches to the old problems.

Nevertheless, work in these programs can have certain troublesome aspects. Foremost probably is the fact that you will be the lone therapist in the district. In some instances there may be two or three of you, but usually you will be cut off from contacts with people who can talk shop with you. To add to the feeling of isolation will be the lack of access to certain professional resources. There may be few, if any, community agencies concerned with the problems of children. Travel, too, must be considered. You may find that the schools are far apart. Do you mind driving in bad weather? And lastly, you will have fewer social contacts although those you do make may be very satisfying. After all, life anywhere does not afford time for a great number of close friends.

Trends in Speech Correction

There are five dominant trends in speech correction today. One is rapid growth, another is the development of various instructional media, the third is increased specialization, the fourth is the growing reduction in case loads, and, finally, a new demand for clinical skills.

Time was (and it is within the memory of the writer) when university departments in speech correction were staffed by one person and even that one might not be giving full time to the work. Time was when the entire membership of our association could be seated at one banquet table and each member be called upon for a few remarks. Time was when the complete publications of the American Speech and Hearing Association consisted of a bound mimeographed copy of speeches made at the annual meeting and published gratis by an interested university. Time was when the business of A.S.H.A. was handled by one professor who, during his spare time, did all the work of keeping the organization together and the channels of communication open.

All this has changed. In many universities speech correction is an independent department staffed by several professors, each a specialist in some one branch of the work. A.S.H.A. now confines its conventions to three or four of the largest cities because only in them can adequate space be found to accommodate the membership. A staff of several professional workers now handles the association's business and several publications keep the members abreast with the rapidly changing picture. All this means that we are members of a profession which has come out of its infancy and its dependency on help from others and has now reached that stage in maturity where it can fend for itself.

The second trend which is becoming increasingly evident in all education is toward using the learning tools and methods which scientists are improving every day. These materials, such as multiple-track tape recorders, audiometers, speech amplifiers, slides, movies, television and radio lessons, delayed side-tone machines, language-masters, opaque and overhead projectors, polygraphs, and others which may be on the market before this book goes to print are all designed to increase the effectiveness of teaching. Self-teaching machines may enable you to do more individual therapy. In work like speech correction where a prime aim is to increase auditory and visual perceptiveness, these materials are of great value. Even though the aids may not decrease your teaching load, they should make your teaching more effective. Yours will be the task to make these communication media real adjuncts to speech therapy.

The third trend is toward increased specialization. As the fund of knowledge concerning the causes and the remedial procedures associated with speech defects expands, it becomes increasingly difficult for one person to be an expert in all phases. As we have noted, this is evidenced by the increase in specialization on university staffs. Even the textbooks are being written by different authors for each specialty. While for some time to come many of us will be and perhaps always should be working with all types of cases, yet we recognize that certain complicated problems may well require the assistance of more highly specialized persons. We may well be regarded as a type of specialized generalists, and as such, need extensive and continuous training. The time spent in earning the baccalaureate degree no longer suffices for the student to acquire the vast fund of knowledge available in our work. For a beginning, yes, a B.S. may still suffice, but every therapist should recognize that graduate work should be started early in his or her career. This applies equally as well to the women as to the men. Look at the world about you and read the statistics. Most women are going to be working outside of their homes during a large portion of their lives. Even with graduate degrees and with the most conscientious of efforts we will be hard put to keep up with the gigantic strides of a space age. But it will be exciting.

The final trends are toward a lower case load and toward a more clinical type of therapy. With the growing interest in speech improvement and with classroom teachers becoming more efficient in aiding speech development, the number of young children requiring speech therapy undoubtedly will decrease. Add to this the number of articulatory cases for whom prognostic screening tests will indicate the probable mastery of normal speech independently of therapy, and with better diagnostic aids in evaluating delayed speech, we can be certain that the therapist's case load (on a percentage of school population basis) will grow lower. Too, there are the results of years of therapy to be considered. It is only in new programs that the old estimate of 8 to 10 per cent of the school population as having defective speech still holds true. In long established programs far fewer speech defectives are found. All facts considered, it is safe to assume that we are going to find an increasingly smaller proportion of children needing speech therapy. In spite of the expanding school enrollment, there may well be more time for individual work. To attain this should be our goal. What our profession has to offer is a clinical service. Let us strive to establish it.

Private Practice

A certain amount of speech therapy, largely with adults or preschool children, is done by private practitioners. You may want to do some private work with cases which cannot be included in the school program. You, of course, will have evenings, Saturdays, holi-

50   What might private practice offer you?
      Paul D. Knight, "Advantages and Disadvantages of Private Practice,"
      Journal of Speech and Hearing Disorders, XII (June 1947), 199-201.

days, and summer vacations free. In addition to augmenting your income, there are some advantages in this type of practice. First, it will give you a chance to do concentrated therapy with an individual who, because he has chosen to come to you and to pay you a fee, will likely give you complete cooperation. Second, these cases are often very interesting because the client has a self-recognized need for help or he would not be with you. A third advantage is that through referrals from physicians, psychologists, clinics, and agencies, you might make some valuable contacts.

When they take leaves of absence to rear families, many therapists find that small private practices help maintain an interest in speech correction, and when the youngest offspring is safely enrolled in school, these therapists return to their jobs. In the meantime therapy is work that can be done in a home, providing there is one quiet room, and young mothers enjoy doing it.

It is not recommended that you attempt *any* private practice during your first years or before you have the necessary graduate training and qualifications. You will have plenty of school work to

keep you busy, and it may be that you are not yet ready to strike
out alone and take the more complicated cases. There are many
pitfalls in private practice.

51 What has been learned in Indiana concerning private practice?
    Raymond Summers, "Private Practice of Public School Therapists in In-
    diana," Journal of Speech and Hearing Disorders, XXIV (February 1959),
    51-54.

Trends in Our Organization

As our profession grows into maturity, inevitable differences of
opinion arise concerning what form our organization should take
and in what directions it should move. There are those who have

52 Why do we have a speech association?
    Robert West, "To Our New Members—Ave et Vale," ASHA, III (January
    1961), 6-8.

believed that the association should serve primarily people who are
interested in basic science and research. Not only do they feel our
journals and convention programs should cater to their interests,
but also that they must be the people to hold the offices and determine the policies. In recent years the therapists have made some
small gains but hardly in proportion to their number in the association. National conventions now have excellent programs devoted
to problems of therapy and the publications of the A.S.H.A. contain
at least a few articles of particular interest to people working with
children. The practicing therapists' names, however, are usually
absent from lists of officers, council members, and committee assignments. In fairness, it must be recognized that the chief reason for
the lack of articles of significance to school therapists is their own
failure to submit any for publication and the fact that few, if any,
therapists have held positions of influence in the association is a
result of their own indifference to organizational affairs. Very few
attend the business meetings and never are there organized efforts to
promote policies or candidates representing the therapist's point of
view.

53 What developments characterize the maturing status of our profession?
    Jon Eisenson, "Coming of Age in a Profession," Journal of Speech and
    Hearing Disorders, XXIV (May 1956), 195-200.

There is a second division, possibly the fastest growing one, within the organization. This group believes that the association must have two groups, those who do the research and those who practice therapy. Each of these groups is part of the whole and neither has much value without the other. Scientific truths must be discovered, but discovery alone is a sterile thing. New facts take on significance only when they go into action and in some manner add effectiveness to human behavior. Therapy will improve only as it utilizes the new ideas discovered by the researchers, but research must be focused on clinical problems or it often becomes pointless. This point of view has been very well expressed by Dr. Margaret Powers.

> 54   Why is it necessary that all members of our profession coordinate their efforts?
>   Margaret Hall Powers, "The Dichotomy of Our Profession," *Journal of Speech and Hearing Disorders*, XX (March 1955), 4-10.

Then there is a third group, those who believe the school therapist can gain more from organizations closely associated with education than from the A.S.H.A. These people argue that we are a part of an over-all organization for the education of handicapped children. That is true. Our money comes from funds allocated for special education. That is true. We are included in administrative and supervisory plans for special education. That, too, is true. One basic factor, however, is lacking in all organizations except the A.S.H.A. It is the inspiration and the knowledge needed for growth in our specific profession, speech correction. We can get these life-giving essentials only from an organization which represents all facets of our own profession. Each member has a responsibility for making the A.S.H.A. an association to serve all of us and to serve us well.

> 55   At what levels of professional preparation have the greatest increases in A.S.H.A. membership come?
>   K. Johnson and P. Newman, "Trends in the Profession," *ASHA*, III (April 1961), 109-14.

So there appears to be no inexpensive or time-saving solution to the therapist's problem of which organizations to join. As a therapist, you need A.S.H.A. As a member of the school general staff and of the special education group, you can profit from joining the educational organizations which represent these people. Your basic allegiance, however, should be with your own professional group. You may as well accept the fact that you are going to have to spend a fair bit of time and money on organizations. But if you put something into them, you'll get something out. Your opportunities for growth will be many.

Trends in General Education

In the long look forward, not only speech correction but all of education appears to be emerging into a profession of considerable stature. The public as well as the profession itself is demanding that all members be well prepared. Recognition of the importance of the work is growing, and although the cost makes it a major item in all taxes, the taxpayer is willing to pay the bill. In doing so, however, he is being more and more insistent that the job be well done.

Our dependence on the support of the public is a good thing. In a democracy education belongs to, and should be controlled by, the people. This intimate relationship with the grass roots makes it imperative that we all be active members of the body politic. Authoritativeness and dictatorships are fast passing from the school scene. More and more members of faculties are going to have responsibilities for determining and executing policies. There is evidence that therapists are leaders in many activities concerning teachers' welfare and growth. Let there be more. Community affairs outside of the school also need your intelligent participation. You are going out into what will be one of the most, if not the most, rapidly changing and exciting era of human history. May you be worthy!

bibliography

1. Ainsworth, S., "Suggestions for a Successful Speech Correction Program in Public Schools," *Quarterly Journal of Speech,* XXXI (December 1945), 471-77.
2. Anderson, Virgil A., *Improving the Child's Speech* (New York: Oxford University Press, Inc., 1953).
3. Artley, A. S., "A Study of Certain Factors Presumed to be Associated with Reading and Speech Difficulties," *Journal of Speech and Hearing Disorders,* XIII (December 1948), 351-60.
4. ———, *Your Child Learns to Read* (Chicago: Scott, Foresman & Co., 1953).
5. Axline, V. A., *Play Therapy* (Boston: Houghton Mifflin Company, 1947).
6. Backus, O., and J. Beasley, *Speech Therapy with Children* (Boston: Houghton Mifflin Company, 1951).
7. Bangs, T., "Evaluating Children with Language Delay," *Journal of Speech and Hearing Disorders,* XXVI (February 1961), 6-18.
8. Beasley, Jane, "Children as Guides to Teaching," *Journal of Speech and Hearing Disorders,* XXII (December 1957), 691-95.

9. Beasley, Jane, "Development of Social Skills as an Instrument in Speech Therapy," *Journal of Speech and Hearing Disorders,* XVI (September 1951), 241-45.

10. ————, *Slow to Talk* (New York: Bureau of Publications, Teachers College, Columbia University, 1956).

11. Bender, James, "Organization and Guiding Principles of the New York City Survey of the Speech Handicapped Children Conducted October 1939," *Journal of Speech Disorders,* V (June 1940), 357-62.

12. Berry, M. R., and Jon Eisenson, *Speech Disorders* (New York: Appleton-Century-Crofts, 1956).

13. Bingham, D., and others, "Public School Speech and Hearing Services: IV. Program Organization and Management," *Journal of Speech and Hearing Disorders,* Monograph Supplement 8 (July 1961), pp. 33-49.

14. Black, Martha E., and others, "Public School Speech and Hearing Services III, Supervision of Speech and Hearing Programs," *Journal of Speech and Hearing Disorders,* Monograph Supplement 8 (July 1961), pp. 22-32.

15. Blanton, Smiley, "Helping the Speech Handicapped School Student," *Journal of Speech Disorders,* I (December 1936), 97-100.

16. Boston, Opal, "School Social Service," *Social Work Year Book* (New York: National Association of Social Workers, 1960).

17. Brazie, G., *Speech Practice Book* (Portland, Ore.: J. K. Gill Company, 1953).

18. Brong, C. Cordelia, "Sigma Alpha Eta," *ASHA,* II (December 1960), 435-36.

19. Brown, Grace T., "Speech Correction in Rochester, New York, Schools," *Journal of Speech Disorders,* XII (September 1947), 334-38.

20. Bryngelson, B., and E. Mikalson, *Speech Correction Through Listening* (Chicago: Scott, Foresman & Company, 1959).

21. Burdin, L. Gray, "Survey of Speech Defects in the Indianapolis Primary Grades," *Journal of Speech Disorders,* V (September 1940), 247-58.

22. Burton, W. H., *The Guidance of Learning Activities* (New York: Appleton-Century-Crofts, 1952).

23. Carhart, Raymond, "Survey of Speech Defects in Illinois High Schools," *Journal of Speech Disorders,* IV (March 1939), 61-70.

24. Carter, Eunice T., and McKenzie Buck, "Prognostic Testing for Functional Articulation Disorders Among Children in the First Grade," *Journal of Speech and Hearing Disorders,* XXIII (May 1958), 124-33.

25. Chapman, M. E., "Speech Clinician and Classroom Teacher Cooperate in a Speech Correction Program," *Journal of Speech Disorders,* VII (March 1942), 57-61.

26. Chapman, M. E., and others, "Public School Speech and Hearing Services, VI, Remedial Procedures," *Journal of Speech and Hearing Disorders,* Monograph Supplement 8 (July 1961), 58-77.

27. Chipman, S., *The Child's Book of Speech Sounds* (Magnolia, Mass.: Expression Company, 1954).

28. Chopin, Alice C., "Speech Correction and Speech Improvement Program in a Large City School System," *Journal of Speech Disorders,* VI (June 1941), 109-10.

29. Crampton, G., *Riddles and Jokes* (New York: Affiliated Publishers, Inc., 1961).

30. Cypreansen, Lucille, *Speech Development, Improvement and Correction* (New York: The Ronald Press Company, 1959).

31. ———, and J. H. Wiley, and L. T. Laase, *Speech Improvement and Correction* (New York: The Ronald Press Company, 1957).

32. Diehl, G. F., and C. D. Stinnett, "Efficiency of Teacher Referrals in a School Speech Testing Program," *Journal of Speech and Hearing Disorders,* XXIV (February 1959), 34-36.

33. Dorfman, Elaine, "Play Therapy" in Carl B. Rogers' *Client-Centered Therapy* (Boston: Houghton Mifflin Company, 1951).

34. Dunn, Harriet M., "Speech and Hearing Program for Children in a Rural Area," *Journal of Speech and Hearing Disorders,* XIV (1949), 166-70.

35. East, Marjorie, *Display for Learning,* E. Dale, ed. (New York: Dryden Press, 1952).

36. Eckelmann, D., and P. Baldridge, "Speech Training for the Child with a Cleft Palate," *Journal of Speech Disorders,* X (June 1945), 137-48.

37. Eisenson, Jon, and Mardel Ogilvie, *Speech Correction in the Schools* (New York: The Macmillan Company, 1957).

38. Emerson, L. S., *Storytelling* (Grand Rapids, Mich.: Zondervan Publishing House, 1959).

39. Enquist, L. E., and C. F. Wagner, "Flannel Chart Technique for the Rehabilitation of Speech and Hearing Disorders," *Journal of Speech and Hearing Disorders,* XV (December 1950), 338-40.

40. Fairbanks, G., *Practical Voice Practice* (New York: Harper & Row, Publishers, 1944).

41. ———, *Voice and Articulation Drill Book,* Rev. Ed. (New York: Harper & Row, Publishers, 1960).

42. Fein, B., and others, "Effective Utilization of Staff Time in Public School Speech Correction," *Journal of Speech and Hearing Disorders,* XXI (September 1956), 283-91.

43. Freeman, G. C., and J. A. Sonnega, "Peer Evaluation of Children in Speech Correction Class," *Journal of Speech and Hearing Disorders,* XXI (June 1956), 179-82.

44. Froeschels, E., and A. Jellinek, *Practice of Voice and Speech Therapy* (Magnolia, Mass.: Expression Company, 1941).
45. Gaitskell, Charles D., *Children and Their Art* (New York: Harcourt, Brace & World, Inc., 1958).
46. Garrison, Geraldine, and others, "Public School Speech and Hearing Services: VII, Speech Improvement," *Journal of Speech and Hearing Disorders*, Monograph Supplement 8 (Júly 1961), pp. 78-92.
47. Geri, P. H., *Illustrated Games and Rhythms for Children* (Englewood Cliffs, N.J.: Prentice-Hall, Inc., 1955).
48. Goldberg, P., and E. Braslow, *Better Speech Can Be Fun* (Magnolia, Mass.: Expression Company, 1960).
49. Green, M. C., *Learning to Babble* (New York: Harper & Row, Publishers, 1960).
50. Hahn, E., "Communication in the Therapy Session," *Journal of Speech and Hearing Disorders*, XXV (February 1960), 19-23.
51. ———, "Role Playing, Creative Dramatics and Play Therapy in Speech Correction," *Speech Teacher*, IV (November 1955), 233-38.
52. Hall, Margaret, "Auditory Factors in Functional Articulatory Speech Defects," *Journal of Experimental Education*, VII (December 1938), 110-32.
53. Hallowel, Davis, and R. S. Silverman, *Hearing and Deafness* (New York: Holt, Rhinehart & Winston, Inc., 1960).
54. Hanley, T. D., and others, "Public School Speech and Hearing Services, XI, Summary: New Horizons," *Journal of Speech and Hearing Disorders*, Monograph Supplement 8 (July 1961), pp. 124-31.
55. Hawk, S. S., "Can a Child Be Taught to Talk?" *Journal of Speech Disorders*, IV (June 1939), 173-79.
56. ———, "Moto-Kinesthetic Training for Children with Speech Handicaps," *Journal of Speech Disorders*, VII (December 1942), 357-60.
57. Hejna, R. F., *Speech Disorders and Non-Directive Therapy* (New York: McGraw-Hill Book Company, 1951).
58. Heltman, H. J., *Trippingly on the Tongue* (New York: Harper & Row, Publishers, 1955).
59. Houchin, Thomas D., "Cooperation in a Public School Speech Correction Program," *Journal of Speech and Hearing Disorders*, XIII (September 1948), 247-50.
60. ———, "Notes on Organizing a Speech Correction Program in the Public Schools," *Journal of Speech and Hearing Disorders*, XIV (March 1949), 53-62.
61. Irwin, R. B., "Oral Language for Slow Learning Children," *Journal of Mental Deficiency*, LXIII (July 1959), 32-40.
62. ———, and others, "Public School Speech and Hearing Services: VIII, Professional Standards and Training," *Journal of Speech and Hearing Disorders*, Monograph Supplement 8 (July 1961), pp. 93-104.

63. Irwin, R. B., *Speech and Hearing Therapy* (Englewood Cliffs, N.J.: Prentice-Hall, Inc., 1953).

64. ———, *A Speech Pathologist Talks to Parents and Teachers* (Pittsburgh: Stanwix House, Inc., 1961).

65. Johnson, W., *People in Quandaries* (New York: Harper & Row, Publishers, 1946).

66. ———, *Speech Problems of Children* (New York: Grune & Stratton, Inc., 1950).

67. ———, F. C. Darley, and D. C. Spriestersbach, *Diagnostic Methods in Speech Pathology* (New York: Harper & Row, Publishers, 1963).

68. ———, and others, *Speech Handicapped School Children* (New York: Harper & Row, Publishers, 1956).

69. Jones, M. V., *Baby Talk* (Springfield, Ill.: Charles C. Thomas, Publisher, 1960).

70. Klingeil, G. M., "The Historical Background of the Modern Speech Clinic: Part I, Stuttering and Stammering," *Journal of Speech Disorders,* IV (June 1939), 115-32.

71. Knight, Edgar W., *Education in the U.S.* (New York: Ginn & Company, 1951).

72. Knight, Helen, and others, "Public School Speech and Hearing Services: II The Public School Clinician: Professional Definition and Relationship," *Journal of Speech and Hearing Disorders,* Monograph Supplement 8 (July 1961), pp. 10-21.

73. Knight, Paul D., "A.S.H.A. and Your Professional Growth," *ASHA,* I (October 1959), 50-52.

74. Koch, Helen I., "Sibling Influence on Children's Speech," *Journal of Speech and Hearing Disorders,* XXI (September 1956), 322-28.

75. Kuhlan, Raymond, and Beatrice Lee, "Personality Characteristics and Social Acceptability in Adolescence," in *Mental Hygiene,* Peter T. Huntras, ed. (Columbus, Ohio: Charles E. Merrill Books, Inc., 1961).

76. Kurtz, Russel H., ed., *Social Work Year Book* (New York: National Association of Social Workers, 1960).

77. Lee, Irving A., *Language Habits in Human Affairs* (New York: Harper & Row, Publishers, 1941).

78. Lillywhite, Herold, "A Point of View for Those Working with the Handicapped," *Exceptional Children,* XXV (November 1958), 101-5.

79. Lorberg, H. Y., Jr., "The Classroom Teacher and the Speech Correction Program," *The Speech Teacher,* IV (January 1955).

80. Louttit, C. M., and E. C. Halls, "Survey of Speech Defects Among the Public School Children of Indiana," *Journal of Speech Disorders,* I (July 1936), 73-80.

81. Low, Gordon, M. Crerar, and Leon Lassers, "Communication Centered Speech Therapy," *Journal of Speech and Hearing Disorders,* XXIV (November 1959), 361-69.

82. Lowell, E. L., N. S. Metfessel, and A. W. McEachern, "Experimental Apparatus for Testing Pre-School Children," *Journal of Speech and Hearing Disorders,* XXIV (May 1959), 212-14.

83. Lowenfeld, Viktor, *Your Child and His Art* (New York: The Macmillan Company, 1954).

84. Luper, Harold L., and S. Ainsworth, "Speech Correction Rooms in the Public Schools," *Exceptional Children,* XXII (October 1955), 24.

85. Luria, A. R., and F. I. A. Yudovich, *Speech and the Development of Mental Processes in the Child* (London: Staples Press, 1959).

86. McCausland, M., M. B. Miller, and I. Okie, *Speech Through Pictures* (Magnolia, Mass.: Expression Company, 1957).

87. McDonald, Eugene T., *Understanding Those Feelings* (Pittsburgh: Stanwix House, Inc., 1962).

88. MacDonald, N. V., ed., "Books Suitable for Small Children," *Volta Review,* LII (January 1950), 73-75.

89. MacLearie, Elizabeth, "Suggestions for Supervised Teaching in Speech Correction," *Journal of Speech Disorders,* XII (December 1947), 369-72.

90. McLaughlin, N., "Uses of the Flannelgraph," *Volta Review,* LIV (September 1952), 317-23.

91. McWilliams, Betty Jane, "Adult Education Program for Mothers of Children with Speech Handicaps," *Journal of Speech and Hearing Disorders,* XXIV (November 1959), 408-10.

92. Matthews, J., E. P. Wade, J. W. Birch, and E. J. Burgi, *The Best Speech Series* (Pittsburgh: Stanwix House, Inc., 1960).

93. Metraux, R. W., "Speech Profiles of the Pre-School Child 18 to 54 Months," *Journal of Speech and Hearing Disorders,* XV (March 1950), 37-53.

94. Milisen, Robert L., "Introducing Speech Correction in a New School System," *Journal of Speech Disorders,* IV (September 1939), 241-45.

95. Molloy, Julia S., *Teaching the Retarded Child to Talk* (New York: The John Day Company, Inc., 1961).

96. Monroe, Marion, *Growing Into Reading* (Chicago: Scott, Foresman & Company, 1951).

97. Morley, M. M., *The Development and Disorders of Speech in Childhood* (Baltimore: The Williams & Wilkins Co., 1957).

98. Morse, William C., "Teacher or Therapist" in *Mental Hygiene,* P. T. Huntras, ed. (Columbus, Ohio: Charles E. Merrill Books, Inc., 1961).

99. Moustakas, C. E., *Children in Play Therapy* (New York: McGraw-Hill Book Company, 1958).

100. Mullendore, James, "Role of Survey and Diagnostic Clinics in a State Program of Speech Correction," *Journal of Speech and Hearing Disorders,* XIV (September 1948), 234-39.

101. Murphy, A. T., and R. M. Fitz Simons, "Music Therapy for the Speech Handicapped," *Elementary School Journal,* LIX (October 1958), 39-45.

102. ———, and R. M. Fitz Simons, *Stuttering and Personality Dynamics* (New York: The Ronald Press Company, 1960).

103. ———, R. M. Fitz Simons, and W. L. Pronovost, *Does Your Pupil Use "Baby Talk"?* (Boston, Mass.: Speech and Hearing Center, Boston University School of Education, 1956).

104. Nemoy, E., *Speech Correction Through Story Telling Units* (Magnolia, Mass.: Expression Company, 1954).

105. Oberman, C. E., "Improving Pupils Speech: A Practical Program of Correction," *Nation's Schools,* XXVIII (December 1941), 51-53.

106. Palmer, M. F., "Managing Overprotective Tendencies with Speech Impaired Children," *Journal of Speech and Hearing Disorders,* XXV (November 1960), 405-8.

107. Parkinson, C. Northcote, *Parkinson's Law* (Boston: Houghton Mifflin Company, 1957).

108. Perlman, Helen Harris, *So You Want to Be A Social Worker* (New York: Harper & Row, Publishers, 1962).

109. Phair, G. M., "Public School Speech and Hearing Services: IX, Recruitment Careers in Speech Pathology and Audiology," *Journal of Speech and Hearing Disorders,* Monograph Supplement 8 (July 1961), pp. 105-13.

110. Pollock, Morris, and Miriam S. Pollock, *The Clown Family Speech Book* (Springfield, Ill.: Charles C. Thomas, Publisher, 1960).

111. Poole, I., "Genetic Development of Articulation of Consonant Sounds in Speech," *Elementary English Review,* XI (June 1934) 159-61.

112. Powers, Margaret Hall, "Auditory Factors in Functional Articulatory Speech Defects," *Journal of Experimental Education,* VII (December 1938), 110-32.

113. ———, "The Dichotomy of Our Profession," *Journal of Speech and Hearing Disorders,* XX (March 1955), 4-10.

114. ———, "What Makes an Effective Public School Speech Therapist?" *Journal of Speech and Hearing Disorders,* XXI (December 1956), 461-67.

115. Pronovost, W., "Survey of Services for Speech and Hearing Handicapped in New England," *Journal of Speech and Hearing Disorders,* XVI (June 1951), 148-56.

116. ———, and others, "Public School Speech and Hearing Services: X, Research Current Status and Needs," *Journal of Speech and Hearing Disorders,* Monograph Supplement 8 (July 1961), pp. 114-23.

117. Quinn, S. B., and E. L. Hutchison, *Listen—Look—Say* (Cambridge, Mass.: Educators Publishing Service, 1960).

118. Reeves, Elizabeth W., "Current Practices and Trends in Speech Correction Certification," *Journal of Speech and Hearing Disorders,* XXIV (February 1959), 7-15.

119. Reid, Gladys, "Efficacy of Speech Re-education of Functional Defectives in the Elementary School," *Journal of Speech Disorders,* XII (September 1947), 301-13.
120. Rigg, M. G., "A Superior Child Who Would Not Talk," *Child Development,* IX (December 1938), 361-62.
121. Roe, V. I., and others, "Public School Speech and Hearing Services: V, Clinical Practice, Diagnosis and Measurement," *Journal of Speech and Hearing Disorders,* Monograph Supplement 8 (July 1961), pp. 50-57.
122. ———, and R. Milisen, "Effect of Maturation upon Defective Articulation in Elementary Grades," *Journal of Speech and Hearing Disorders,* VII (March 1942), 37-50.
123. Rogers, Carl B., *Client-Centered Therapy* (Boston: Houghton Mifflin Company, 1951).
124. Ronnei, E. C., *Learning to Look and Listen* (New York: Bureau of Publications, Columbia University Teachers College, 1951).
125. Russell, D. H., *Children Learn to Read* (New York: Ginn & Company, 1949).
126. ———, *Reading Aids Through the Grades* (New York: Bureau of Publications, Columbia University Teachers College, 1957).
127. ———, and E. F. Russell, *Listening Aids Through the Grades* (New York: Bureau of Publications, Columbia University Teachers College, 1959).
128. Sayler, Helen K., "Effect of Maturation upon Defective Articulation in Grades Seven through Twelve," *Journal of Speech and Hearing Disorders,* XIV (September 1949), 202-7.
129. Schoolfield, L. D., *Better Speech and Better Reading* (Magnolia, Mass.: Expression Company, 1951).
130. ———, and J. Timberlake, *Sounds the Letters Make* (Boston: Little, Brown & Co., 1940).
131. Schuell, Hildred, "Working with Parents of Stuttering Children," *Journal of Speech and Hearing Disorders,* XIV (September 1949), 251-54.
132. ———, "Working with Speech Defectives in the Public Schools," *Journal of Speech Disorders,* VIII (December 1943), 355-62.
133. Scott, L. B., "Puppetry," *American Childhood,* XLII (October 1956), 13-15.
134. ———, and J. J. Thompson, *Rhymes for Fingers and Flannelboard* (St. Louis: Webster Publishing Company, 1960).
135. ———, and J. J. Thompson, *Speech Ways* (St. Louis: Webster Publishing Company, 1955).
136. ———, and J. J. Thompson, *Talking Time* (St. Louis: Webster Publishing Company, 1951).
137. ———, and L. F. Wood, *Singing Fun* (St. Louis: Webster Publishing Company, 1955).

138. Suydam, V. R., "Speech Survey Methods in the Public Schools," *Journal of Speech and Hearing Disorders,* XIII (March 1948), 51-54.
139. Shames, George H., "Use of Nonsense Syllables in Articulation Therapy," *Journal of Speech and Hearing Disorders,* XXII (June 1957), 261-63.
140. Shelton, R. L., and W. Diedrich, "Use of Short Loops of Recording Tape," *Journal of Speech and Hearing Disorders,* XXVI (May 1961), 181-82.
141. Sisters of St. Francis of Assisi, *A Beginner's Speech Book* (Milwaukee, Wis.: St. John's School for the Deaf, 1959).
142. Sommers, Raymond, "Private Practice of Public School Speech Therapists in Indiana," *Journal of Speech and Hearing Disorders,* XXIV (February 1959), 51-54.
143. ———, C. Cockerille, C. D. Paul, D. C. Bowser, G. R. Fichmer, A. K. Fenton, and F. G. Coperas, "Effects of Speech Therapy and Speech Improvement upon Articulation and Reading," *Journal of Speech and Hearing Disorders,* XXVI (February 1961), 27-38
144. Sondel, Bess, *The Humanity of Words* (Cleveland, Ohio: World Publishing Company, 1958).
145. Steer, M. D., "Public School Speech and Hearing Services," *Journal of Speech and Hearing Disorders,* Monograph Supplement 8 (July 1961).
146. Stinchfield, S. M., and E. H. Young, *Children with Delayed or Defective Speech* (Stanford, Calif.: Stanford University Press, 1938).
147. Stoddard, C. B., "Public School Approach to the Treatment of Stuttering," *Journal of Speech Disorders,* IV (September 1939), 219-22.
148. ———, *Sounds for Little Folks* (Magnolia, Mass.: Expression Company, 1940).
149. Strazzulla, M., "A Language Guide for the Parents of Retarded Children," *American Journal of Mental Deficiency,* LIX (July 1954), 48-58.
150. Suttles, P. H., ed., *Elementary Teachers Guide to Free Curriculum Materials* (Randolph, Wis.: Educators Progress Service, 1960).
151. Sutton, Eddie, "Integrating Speech Therapy with Language Arts in the Elementary School," *Journal of Speech and Hearing Disorders,* XX (December 1955), 376-79.
152. Taeuber, Conrad, "Some Current Population Trends in the United States," and "Financing Education for Our Changing Population" (Committee on Educational Finance, National Education Association), p. 18.
153. Templin, Mildred, "Possibilities of Research for the Public School Speech Therapist," *Journal of Speech and Hearing Disorders,* XVIII (December 1953), 355-59.
154. Tjomsland, L. M., "Santa's Speech Toys," *The Speech Teacher,* V (November 1956), 309-12.

155. Travis, L. E., ed., *Handbook of Speech Pathology* (New York: Appleton-Century-Crofts, 1958).

156. ———, and D. W. Baruch, *Personal Problems of Everyday Life* (New York: Appleton-Century-Crofts, 1941).

157. Tufts, L. C., and A. R. Holliday, "Effectiveness of Trained Parents as Speech Therapists," *Journal of Speech and Hearing Disorders,* XXIV (November 1959), 395-401.

158. Van Riper, C., *A Case Book in Speech Therapy* (Englewood Cliffs, N.J.: Prentice-Hall, Inc., 1953).

159. ———, *Speech Correction: Principles and Methods* (Englewood Cliffs, N.J.: Prentice-Hall, Inc., 1963).

160. ———, *Speech Therapy: A Book of Reading* (Englewood Cliffs, N.J.: Prentice-Hall, Inc., 1953).

161. ———, *Teaching Your Child to Talk* (New York: Harper & Row, Publishers, 1950).

162. ———, *Your Child's Speech Problems* (New York: Harper & Row, Publishers, 1961).

163. ———, and J. V. Irwin, *Voice and Articulation* (Englewood Cliffs, N.J.: Prentice-Hall, Inc., 1958).

164. Warkomski, R. C., and R. B. Irwin, *Play and Say* (Pittsburgh, Pa.: Stanwix House, Inc., 1961).

165. Webb, C., and J. Parnell, "Unit Teaching in Speech and Hearing at Elementary School Level," *Journal of Speech and Hearing Disorders,* XXV (August 1960), 302.

166. Weiss, D. A., "Speech in Retarded Children," *Nervous Child,* IX (January 1951), 21-30.

167. Weissberg, Albert, "Guide to Audio-Visual Materials in Speech and Hearing Disorders," *Journal of Speech and Hearing Disorders,* Monograph Supplement 2 (September 1952), pp. 1-86.

168. Wood, Nancy E., "Identifying Speech Disorders in the Classroom," *School Life* (U.S. Department of Health, Education, and Welfare), XIV, No. 5 (March 1963), 6-8.

169. West, Robert, "The Association in Historical Perspective," *ASHA,* II (January 1960), 8-11.

170. ———, "To Our New Members, Ave et Vale," *ASHA,* III (January 1961), 6-8.

171. ———, M. Ansberry, and A. Carr, *The Rehabilitation of Speech,* 3rd Ed. (New York: Harper & Row, Publishers, 1957).

172. White, Alice Mary, and M. H. Harris, *The School Psychologist* (New York: Harper & Row, Publishers, 1961).

173. Willey, Norman R., "Public School Speech and Hearing Therapy Facilities," *Exceptional Children,* XXVIII (November 1961), 129.

174. Wilson, Betty Ann, "Development and Evaluation of a Speech Improvement Program for Kindergarten Children," *Journal of Speech and Hearing Disorders,* XIX (February 1954), 4-13.

175. Wilson, D. K., "Children with Vocal Nodules," *Journal of Speech and Hearing Disorders,* XXVI (February 1961), 19-28.

176. ———, H. S. Ginott, and S. L. Berger, "Group Interview: Initial Parental Clinic Contact," *Journal of Speech and Hearing Disorders,* XXIV (August 1959), 282-84.

177. Wolf, F. W., and G. A. Kelder, *Sounds I Say* (Moravia, N.Y.: Chronicle Guidance Publications, Inc., 1960).

178. Wolfbein, Seymour L., "Social and Economic Implications of Our Rapidly Changing Population," and "Financing Education for Our Changing Population" (Committee on Educational Finance, National Education Association), p. 18.

179. Wood, A. L., *The Jingle Book* (New York: E. P. Dutton & Co., Inc., 1946).

180. ———, *Sound Games* (New York: E. P. Dutton & Co., Inc., 1948).

181. Wood, Kenneth S., "Parental Maladjustment and Functional Articulatory Defects in Children," *Journal of Speech Disorders,* XI (December 1946), 255-75.

182. Wright, Herbert N., "Reliability of Evaluations During Basic Articulation and Stimulation Testing," *Journal of Speech and Hearing Disorders,* Monograph Supplement 4 (December 1954).

183. Young, E. H., and S. S. Hawk, *Moto-Kinesthetic Speech Training* (Stanford, Calif.: Stanford University Press, 1955).

184. Young, J. A., "Speech Rehabilitation in the Rural Schools of Waukesha County Wisconsin," *Journal of Speech Disorders,* X (June 1946), 133-35.

185. Zachry, Caroline B., *Emotions and Conduct in Adolescence* (New York: Appleton-Century Crofts, 1940).

186. Zedler, E. Y., *Listening for Speech Sounds* (New York: Harper & Row, Publishers, 1955).

index